A GUIDE TO
COUNTRYSIDE
CONSERVATION

BRITAIN'S RURAL HERITAGE

WI

LIFE &
LEISURE

A GUIDE TO
COUNTRYSIDE
CONSERVATION

BRITAIN'S RURAL HERITAGE

Dr John Feltwell

WARD LOCK LIMITED
LONDON

First published 1989
© WI Books Ltd 1989
Photography (inside) © John Feltwell: Wildlife Matters 1989

This edition first published in Great Britain in 1989
by Ward Lock, Villiers House, 41/47 Strand,
London WC2N 5JE, England

A Cassell imprint

Reprinted 1991

Acknowledgements

The author would like to thank the following for permission to reproduce
material: the Countryside Commission; Franklyn Perring; Penny Kitchen;
Editor of Home & Country and the author of the poem on page 56
whom it has not been possible to trace.

Editors Suzanne Luchford and Anna Mumford
Commissioning Editor Hilary Wharton
Line illustrations Wendy Bramall
Photographs Wildlife Matters Photographic Library
Cover photograph Jhon Kevern
Cover prints: *front left* David Woodfall NHPA;
front right Michael Leach NHPA; *back* Robert Thrift
National Trust Photographic Library
Designed by Anita Ruddell

Text set in Goudy Old Style by MS Filmsetting Limited, Frome, Somerset
Colour reproduction by Tennon and Polert Colour Scanning Ltd
Printed and bound in Hong Kong by Everbest

British Library Cataloguing in Publication Data
Feltwell, John, 1948–
Countryside conservation.—(WI life and
leisure).
1. Great Britain. Countryside. Conservation
I. Title   II. Series
333.76′16′0941

ISBN 1 85079 186 4

LIST OF
CONTENTS

Everlasting pea

INTRODUCTION

*T*his book is not about gloom, doom, death and destruction. That has all beeen said before. It is about the constructive side of conservation, how wildlife is prospering in the agricultural environment, along motorways, railways and canals, in towns and cities, and how the landscape and wildlife will change.

It is also a book to help you unravel some of the jargon of conservation – a question of interpretation. Some farmers find themselves in situations in which they are encouraged not to farm, even paid to stop farming. It all becomes a little confusing.

The more intensive, or extensive, agriculture becomes, the more wildlife, what is left of it, is obliged to fit tidily into the nature reserves, Sites of Special Scientific Interest (SSSIs) and any man-made habitats available to it. Let us hope that it does.

MEADOWS

Meadows are an integral part of English village life. Most of the villages of Britain grew up around a stream which provided essential water for drinking and washing. It also brought new life to the land and deposited rich alluvial silt. Our sheep grew fat on lush grass, the hay smelt particularly good and our crops benefited from their free annual wash of nutrients. 'Pastures' were for grazing animals, 'meadows' were for gathering hay. This was an age before artificial fertilisers when the air was full of the sound of corncrakes and the hum of honey-bees.

As we cut down the wildwoods for fuel and posts we opened up new habitats for wild flowers. Several of the woodland flowers persisted in the open for some time, eventually giving way to hardier species which thrived and were not dependent upon sunlight. Our medieval meadows would have been a real feast for our eyes today, packed with a colourful variety of species that are now so much of our rural, floral past. We now try to establish what the medieval farmers tried to avoid.

· GLEBE MEADOWS ·

It was the church which owned many of the meadows around the village. These were the closely coveted 'glebe lands' on which rent had to be paid to graze animals, grow food or cut hay. It included the churchyards which were simply enclosures of ancient pastures, and the cemeteries which were a more recent addition. The glebe rent was traditionally paid annually, much of it in produce at the 'tythe' house or barn. Sheaths of corn, pigs, honey and bread all made their way to the owners of the richest village meadows – the clergy. Today the word 'glebe' lands still persists in the name of houses, roads and meadows around the church, reminding us all of our tie with the soil. 'Meads' and 'medes' are with us too.

Churchyards and cemeteries have always been a great refuge for wildlife and it was William Robinson (1838–1935), the father of wild flower gardening, who first published a book called *God's Acre* recognising this fact. Thanks to *The Times* garden writer, Francesca Greenoak, that title has been brought up to date in her masterly appreciation of the subject.

• WATER MEADOWS •

The essence of a water meadow was simple. The stream was either dammed up and the contours of the land used to hold the water, or channels and sluices were made to raise or lower the water. In either case the water flooded on to the flat land carrying with it vital nutrients. Fifty acres (20ha) could be flooded at a time. The water of the chalk streams, especially in Hampshire, where the practice was especially well executed during the seventeenth and eighteenth centuries, was warm (55°F/13°C all year) and made the grass grow under water. The maximum use of water meadows was made. As soon as the water was sluiced off, the sheep would come in. A 1-a (0·4-ha) meadow could feed 400 ewes with lambs for a day, then they would be moved on. The first of a maximum of four crops of hay could be taken from the very best meadows and during the autumn and winter, bullocks put on to graze. All this intensive use of the land still maintained a rich flora of nearly 90 plant species known from nineteenth-century records.

• CHANGING MEADOWS •

Centuries ago, access to the village meadows was unrestricted; much of it was common land. Children played and adults strolled over the water meadows next to the wood. Everyone knew when to keep off, particularly if the meadow was 'up for hay' – standing undisturbed ready for cutting the hay – or if the farmer had chicken or pheasant coops on the meadow. Footpaths and bridlepaths criss-crossed the countryside and provided access points across idyllic meadows. Are we to believe that footpaths were the working-man's routes between pubs which have been preserved today? This is one suggestion.

Shakespeare was so taken with the ways of the living world that he incorporated many examples into his writings. His two-day journeys from Stratford to London would have taken him through the Forest of Arden and alongside many delightful meadows. No wonder he was enamoured of the living world as he came into contact with so much of it. We would call him a keen amateur naturalist today since he was familiar with at least fifty species of bird and many wild plants; putting us all to shame in the depth of his knowledge.

With the enclosures of the land came fences across meadows and intensive grazing. This led to some delicate species dying off. Prickly hawthorn, sloe, wild briar rose and bramble defeated animals' soft palates and were used as hedges or grew as scrub. Thistles and sow-thistles defended themselves with spines, nettles with stings. The quality of the meadow changed. New species became dominant.

Gypsies traditionally lived on common ground, much of it on heaths and commons where flower-rich meadows occurred. Gradually the floral composition of meadows changed with the varied interaction of man. Introduced species from abroad found the meadow habitat to their liking. Our wild flowers became threatened. Aliens crept in, but not many, since most of the native British wild flowers still predominate in a typical English meadow.

Increased mechanisation started to obliterate the delightful furrow and ridges typical of ancient meadows once ploughed with the horse. The horse team would do a figure-of-eight manoeuvre at the hedgerow and return to throw the sod up the other side. The 'lazy beds' of Ireland left their mark too on meadows where potatoes once grew, with deep trenches to soak away the excess water. Ant hills pock-marked ancient meadows to such an extent it was impossible to ride over them without the horse stumbling. Such signs of antiquity, perhaps 1,000 years old, have disappeared from many of our parish meadows.

Gone too are the fields left fallow in the age-old tradition of crop rotation. One year of respite given to a meadow to grow its own complement of wild flowers was given in return for three or four years of hard work and nutrients taken out of it. It was the floral richness of the meadow, with its roots, fibre and organic matter which helped the farmer produce his crops. Now the process is speeded along chemically since artificial phosphates and nitrates reduce an unproductive 12 months down to a few hours.

Strip farming was an old method of cultivation used for the gathering of hay on hay meadows. It is of Saxon origin and was a technique used to apportion the fruits of good land fairly amongst the community. As the wild woods were cleared the land was equally divided amongst the parishioners for cultivation. Strips of land 220yd (200m) long and 22yd (20m) wide were apportioned. This was the old furlong or 'cultura'. Commonly only a half (110yd/100m) or a third (73yd/6.6m) of a furlong was used. One or two large fields would have been divided amongst the workers so that everyone had a share in the better parts of the land. Each strip was divided from the next by a double furrow. The old method of strip farming has left its mark on the land and, in places it is revealed from aerial photographs. Fields with these marks should be conserved wherever possible. They may be the most valuable hay meadows in any community.

The ancient tradition of strip farming is remembered in a few small Oxfordshire villages. The villagers of Begbroke, Wolvercote and Yarnton still relive the ancient practice of selling off the rights to its coveted hay meadows each year. The meadows in question are West Mead and Pixey Mead. Oxhay meadow has fallen victim to a bypass. Owners of the rights to cut hay can then sell off the rights to others and this is done as near to the 29 June as the ripe crop permits. The following week everyone proceeds to the meadows where ancient 'Mead Balls', each with the name of the portion of the meadow and its size (measured on the unit of how much a man could scythe in a day), are brought out, and the initials of the owners of the rights are cut in the hay. Cutting then starts immediately.

Harvest complete, this was a good time to view future prospects safe in the knowledge that the crop was stored away. Merrymaking was the order of the day and much ado was had by village folk, fresh from the fields. For the young men of Lisdoonvarna, a spa town in County Clare, Eire, the period immediately after harvest-time was devoted to finding a bride. Men still flock to the special match-making hotels of Lisdoonvarna with the intent of drinking well and finding a suitable bride, banking on their good harvests.

◆ TYPICAL MEADOW PLANTS ◆

There are two things that can be said about typical meadow plants. Firstly, they are nearly all native British species, and secondly, they are mostly very colourful. The gay abandon of meadow plants does actually have some order to it. If you look at a meadow in May you are greeted with a veritable forest of vegetation. Tall plants tower above a mid-height layer of plants and below these is a myriad of colour made up from speedwells, eyebrights and tiny stitchworts. Seeds shower the ground to start off next year's wild flower display.

Milton was fond of daisies:

Of all the floures in the mede,
Than love I most these floures white and rede,
Soch that men callen daisies in our town.
> Milton *Prologue of the Legend of Good
Women*, 1. 41.

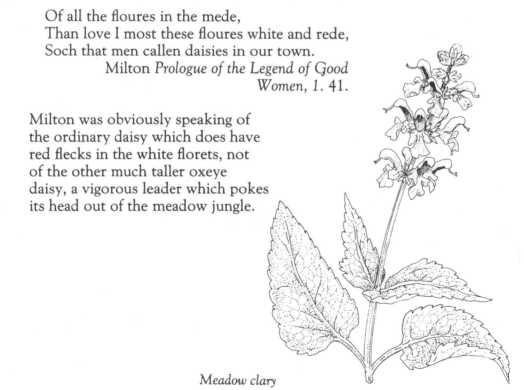

Milton was obviously speaking of
the ordinary daisy which does have
red flecks in the white florets, not
of the other much taller oxeye
daisy, a vigorous leader which pokes
its head out of the meadow jungle.

Meadow clary

SOME MEADOW PLANTS WITH
◆ MEADOW NAMES ◆

If you are interested in the Latin names of plants then a clue to where they live comes from their second name. If it reads *pratensis*, this is a sure sign that the species is a meadow-loving plant, as *pratum* is Latin for meadow.

Apart from the Latin *pratensis* plants which are included in this list, other plants which have meadow in their English name have been selec-

ted. Of course *not all* meadow plants have 'meadow' or '*pratensis*' or *pratense* in their name. This list is selective. England is unique in having such a wealth of common names for wild flowers (some species have over 100 names), many of which pre-date Carl Linnaeus' Latin classifications of the mid-1700s. We have much to learn from common names.

◆ WILD FLOWERS ◆

Common name	Latin name
Meadowbright (usually called marsh marigold or king cups)	*Caltha palustris*
Meadow buttercup	*Ranunculus* several species
Meadow clary	*Salvia pratensis*
Meadow cranesbill	*Geranium pratense*
Meadowflower, or Meadow Kerses (usually called cuckoo flower or milk maids)	*Cardamine pratensis*
Meadow pink (usually called ragged-robin)	*Lychnis flos-cuculi*
Meadowsweet, meadow-maid, maid-of-the-meadow, queen of the meadow	*Filipendula ulmaria*
Meadow rue	*Thalictrum flavum*
Meadow vetchling	*Lathyrus pratensis*
Meadow rocket (usually called early marsh orchid)	*Dactylorchis incarnata*
Meadow saffron	*Colchicum autumnale*
Red clover	*Trifolium pratense*
Goat's beard (usually called Jack-go-to-bed-at-noon, as its flower closes up at midday!)	*Tragopogon pratensis*

◆ GRASSES ◆

Common name	Latin name
Early meadow grass	*Poa infirma*
Meadow barley	*Hordeum secalinum*
Meadow brome	*Bromus commutatus*
Meadow cat's-tail	*Phleum pratense*
Meadow fescue	*Festuca pratensis*
Meadow foxtail	*Alopecurus pratensis*
Meadow oat-grass	*Helictotrichon pratense*
Meadow soft grass (usually called Yorkshire fog)	*Holcus lanatus*
Meadow-grass	*Poa pratensis*

Grasses are the principal group of plants represented in meadows. Giving body and pastel background shades of green and brown to the meadow, they also contribute to the pollen count and hay fever. Their enthusiastic production of pollen is such that millions of pollen grains are released to the wind as it races through the meadow. About a quarter of all meadow plants are grasses. The early flowering ones of April are sweet vernal grass and meadow foxtail whilst the majority which contribute to hay fever problems flower in May and June. Plenty of other plants of the meadow are dispersed by wind, especially the feathery seeds of the daisy family.

When people think of meadows they may conjure up different coloured meadows in their minds: white, yellow or blue ones. The types of plants which grow in meadows depend upon the kind of soil, the pH (a measure of the hydrogen ions in the soil) and how wet or dry the site is. Plants have a brilliant ability to colonise new ground and sometimes produce a spectacular colour display, for instance a meadow of common daisies (signifying nutrient-poor soils), a yellow blaze of buttercups, drifts of sea pinks on the sparse coastal grassland or a meadow full of dandelions or ragwort. Unwanted, ragwort is a poisonous ingredient in dried hay. Curiously, animals are not poisoned by fresh ragwort when it grows in the field since they can detect its poisonous nature and leave it well alone. Dried, the poisonous alkaloids are tasteless.

To study a year in the life of a flowering meadow would be a worthwhile project to embark upon. It sometimes appears that nature produces a natural monoculture of wild flowers at certain times of the year. The meadow may be dominated with one particular species of plant, in what is actually a species-rich site. Different plants take it in stages to flower through the spring and summer. Perhaps a sequence of flowering in an ancient meadow might be pink fritillaries, yellow dandelions, white stitchworts and oxeye daisies, then the yellow of the parasitic yellow rattle.

Clover and lucerne fields are virtually a thing of the past in Britain. Fields traditionally left fallow would suddenly burst forth in July with white clover, providing a feast of flowers for honey-bees. The nectar only 'runs' from clover when the temperature remains in the eighties (F), which is not very often in English summers. Pure clover honey is hard to find now. Clover and lucerne were also grown as a crop since their underground root nodules are rich in nitrogen and these were ploughed into the ground to increase its fertility. Colourful meadows like these were once a real paradise for insects, particularly migratory butterflies, thirsty on their long travels across country from the continent.

Meadowsweet is an attractive addition to the meadow and roadside ditches, particularly with its creamy nodding heads (hence the Latin genus *Filipendula*) which can be seen a long way off. The plant will only grow where it is damp and sadly it has declined as many boggier places have been drained. The species can be regarded as a very important plant since it contains chemicals (including salicylic aldehyde) which are important ingredients of aspirins. These are released when leaves of meadowsweet are crushed giving it its characteristic sweet smell. The species was once known in the genus called *Spiraea* and it is from this name that the word 'aspirin' was coined.

Although we have this wild spiraea of the meadows and hedgerow edges, we still keep plenty of other much more flowery spiraeas going in the garden habitat.

Meadowsweet's sweet smell was also put to good use as a 'strewing' herb, cut and cast over the floor to make the room smell sweet, a custom very much approved by Queen Elizabeth I. Its old name of Queen of the Meadow recalls its former name of *Regina prati* and it was once used at weddings.

Boggier meadows not only sprout the meadowsweet and cuckoo flower but, if you are lucky the marsh marigold. It loves the very damp meadows adjacent to old railway lines and flowers madly in wet woods as well. Rushes and sedges do very well in meadows that keep moist all year. Close to streams in that squelchy inaccessible area the yellow flag, our common wild iris and water dropwort grow side by side. On the mud will be growing the blue brooklime or beccabunga after its Latin name.

Knee deep in flowers, you may find swathes of creamy bedstraw – it was used for stuffing pillows – or patches of ragged-robin, now sadly declined, patches of the commoner orchids, such as early purple, common spotted or the green-winged orchid. These are some of the most common orchids to be found, at least in southern England.

Umbellifers like water dropwort are always difficult to sort out in meadows. All of them have flat or bevelled 'umbels' of flowers borne on long stems; the size of the plant also varies. The most common is cow parsley, or Queen Anne's lace after its flowers, which start to sprout up in the preceding November. Wild carrot meadows can be found in some places. It is best to pinch some of the leaves or flowers to ascertain the typical carrot smell for identification. Coastal meadows may have the low-growing and much more infrequent wild parsnip.

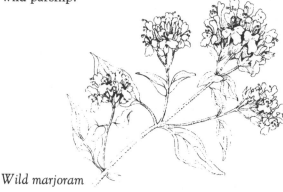

Wild marjoram

◆ ANCIENT MEADOWS ◆

Curiously, ancient meadows are often inadvertently conserved by man, or rather his grazing animals. Meadows left without any grazing animals will soon develop scrubby bushes and trees. All the lovely meadow flowers will disappear in favour of woodland species. An ancient meadow treated with selective broad-leaf herbicide will lose all its 'interesting' flora, otherwise thought of as weeds.

An ancient meadow treated with fertilizer makes the land nutrient-rich, which is bad for the plants we associated with them. Cutting and leaving the hay in the field to rot down also makes the field nutrient-rich. Our precious meadow plants like nutrient-poor conditions. They cannot compete with vigorous grasses which like nutrient-rich conditions. Grazing animals are good conservation tools, usefully brought in during the autumn to eat off the old plant material. Taking the hay each year is good too. Both grazing and hay-taking subdue the natural invasion of a meadow with scrub which would otherwise obscure and eventually eliminate the colourful wild flowers.

Red clover

◆ CRICKLADE ◆

North Meadow, is the best site for the snake's head fritillary in Britain. It is beside the Wiltshire village of Cricklade on the banks of the River Thames which is about 20ft (6m) wide here.

The site is open to the public all year but has restricted access, so as not to disturb the plants, during spring and summer. North Meadow is designated as a National Nature Reserve and is managed by the Nature Conservancy Council (NCC). It is also a Site of Special Scientific Interest. There is a descriptive leaflet about Cricklade obtainable from the interpretive branch of the NCC.

North Meadow is a huge 107a (43ha), rather like a large deserted aerodrome especially when the dandelions are in full flower in May. This is not perhaps what you might expect from one of the finest meadows in Britain. It is edged by the Thames and the River Chum, has a few shallow drainage ditches, untidy hedgerows and many fine pollarded willows (see page 25) around the margin. So popular is the site that visitors tread a well-worn path along the meadow paths, some of which are studded with small stone markers.

These stones are an indication of the long-term management of the meadow. They represent the ownership of strips of land apportioned by the 'hayward' (the man in charge of fences and enclosures) of the local village and some of them carry owners initials. Grazing was, and still is permitted by villagers on this land to protect their common grazing rights from the 12 August to the 12 February. It is an old system called 'lammas' which has its roots in law.

North Meadow has been 'preserved' like this because of its old haymaking and grazing laws. There are more fritillaries here than anywhere else in Britain, in the order of several millions. Many fritillary-rich sites like this would have thrived along the banks of the meandering Thames, but have since been lost due to land improvement. It is thought that North Meadow has remained undisturbed like this for 800 years, uniquely conserving its flora and fauna. It has over 200 species of plant.

The ground is studded with the adder's tongue fern, another indicator of ancient pastures, but also growing here are the burnet saxifrage with its carrot-like leaves, self-heal, forget-me-not, lady's bedstraw, meadowsweet, oxeye daisy, cowslips, marsh marigolds and lady's smock. The Thames is full of pike, perch and chub, the meadow full of small dragonflies, damselflies and butterflies and the bird life is equally rich.

Different parts of North Meadow are harvested for wild flower seed each year as a viable agricultural crop. New types of machines go gently through the meadow in July sucking off the delicate seed. Much of this appears in the shops as 'Cricklade mixture'.

Some of the 200 species of Cricklade's wild flowers whose seed is marketed in genuine Cricklade wild flower seed mixtures.

Common name	Latin name
Autumnal hawkbit	*Leontodon autumnalis*
Bird's foot trefoil	*Lotus corniculatus*
Black medick	*Medicago lupulina*
Cock's foot	*Dactylis glomerata*
Common daisy	*Bellis perennis*
Common sorrel	*Rumex acetosa*
Crested dog's tail	*Cynosurus cristatus*
Dandelion	*Taraxacum officinale*
Fairy flax	*Linum catharticum*
Fiorin	*Agrostis stolonifera*
Goat's beard	*Tragopogon pratensis*
Greater knapweed	*Centaurea scabiosa*
Great burnet	*Sanguisorba officinalis*
Meadowsweet	*Filipendula ulmaria*
Meadow brome	*Bromus commutatus*
Meadow buttercup	*Ranunculus acris*
Meadow fescue	*Festuca pratensis*
Oxeye daisy	*Leucanthemum vulgare*
Pepper-saxifrage	*Silaum silaus*
Perennial rye grass	*Lolium perenne*
Quaking grass	*Briza media*
Red clover	*Trifolium pratense*
Red fescue	*Festuca rubra*
Ribwort plantain	*Plantago lanceolata*
Rough meadow grass	*Poa trivialis*
Selfheal	*Prunella vulgaris*
Smooth meadow grass	*Poa pratensis*
Snake's head fritillary	*Fritillaria meleagris*
Sweet vernal grass	*Anthoxanthum odoratum*
Tufted hair-grass	*Deschampsia cespitosa*
White clover	*Trifolium repens*
Yellow oat-grass	*Trisetum flavescens*
Yellow rattle	*Rhinanthus minor*
Yorkshire fog	*Holcus lanatus*

◆ Species richness

The floristic richness of such ancient meadows is astounding. There may be over 150 species of wild flower in a single meadow, including orchids and ferns. On chalk grassland, such as the Downs or Chilterns the flora may include up to fifty species in every square yard. That is incredibly rich. Imagine you are sitting on the Downs having a picnic; immediately around you you should find all these species. Of course, they will not all be in flower at the same time and you will have to be a competent botanist to identify them all at one time. However, they are all there on a few select sites on ancient pastures. This fragile suite of plants develops over thousands of years, and can so easily be removed by ploughing or herbiciding in just a few minutes.

◆ Rare wild flowers and indicator species

There are certain wild flowers of meadows which, if found, are indicative of an ancient site. Most are sensitive to any slight change or disturbance to the habitat and will soon die off. Thus their presence indicates that you may have discovered an old site, unploughed, unfertilized and undisturbed by man. It may well have been kept open as a meadow by virtue of grazing over the centuries. There are still ancient meadows to be explored in Britain today.

It is in lime-rich soils that the pasqueflower flourishes, sadly in only a few localities in half a dozen counties. Named after the French for Easter (*Pacques*) it flowers in the spring. Being so sensitive to change it has declined rapidly from so many of its former localities. Most of us have seen this species in the garden, where it is conserved, rather than in the wild.

One of the botanical gems of meadows is the snake's head fritillary, now severely threatened in Britain. There is some doubt as to whether it is a native of Britain or not, since this attractive species has been purposely moved around and naturalised in many places. One of the few famous places for it are the meadows of Magdalen College, Oxford, but its finest place is the noted Cricklade meadows. It has a great ability to get itself well established in shady areas, often below trees with not too much grass, and many gardens and estates have fritillaries in a naturalised condition. It likes water-logged sites, thus suggesting its preference for water meadows. Its corms only live about 10 years so it must have unploughed meadows where its seeds can germinate.

Pasqueflower   Snake's head fritillary

Like the butterflies with the same name, fritillaries are named after their spottedness. The drooping flower head is like a spotted snake's head and in a meadow of flowers the petal colours of the plant range from white to dark purple. As the season progresses the elongating stems bear the fruits high for seed dispersal.

Today, we can all buy the corms of snake's head fritillary, lady slipper orchid and pasqueflower from garden centres and all are successful in the garden or conservatory. We are all helping to keep these two 'indicators' of ancient meadows alive at home.

Another botanical treat is the adder's tongue fern which is another indicator of ancient meadows, its wavy tongue curls up higher and higher like that of an arum lily as the season progresses. Another meadow plant, though more often now found in gardens, is the blue-flowered Jacob's ladder.

Wild flowers like these are becoming more vulnerable every day. Britain only has 1,423 native species of plant (the rest are introduced ones) and it is thought that one species of higher or lower plant (e.g. fungus or lichen) is lost from Britain each year. Three-hundred and seventeen species or sub-species are on the danger list and are listed in the British Red Data Book for Vascular Plants (see page 146). They represent about eighteen per cent of Britain's native flora. The greatest numbers of species have been lost from wetlands, then grasslands and

These flowers and grasses are typical of an ancient meadow.

Jacob's ladder

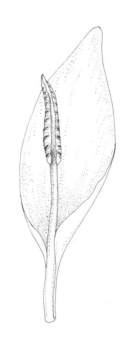

Adder's tongue fern

woodlands thereafter. All habitats are in danger of losing plants. Fifty species of wild plants have become extinct in Lincolnshire in the last forty years. The choice between potatoes or wild plants, for the domestic gardener, is a crucial one.

Staffordshire has lost a staggering 130 species of plant since 1800, Northumberland 124, and East Kent 114. Some of these more indicative plant species are offered protection under Schedule 8 of the Wildlife and Countryside Act 1981, including the military and monkey orchids and the early and late spider orchids. Curiously, two important meadow plants, the pasqueflower and the snake's head fritillary, are not on the protected list but are highly indicative of ancient meadows. To be classifed in the Red Data Book the plants have to occur in less than fifteen 6.2×6.2mi (10×10km) distribution squares. These squares are the way botanists divide the country up to make their dot distribution maps.

You can play a part in helping to stop this trend by assisting your local nature conservation trusts with site reports. The Royal Society for Nature Conservation recommends that more money goes to the Nature Conservancy Council for Sites of Special Scientific Interest (SSSIs, see page 141) scheduling and site monitoring, and to look into re-creation of meadows. There are 1,680 nature reserves protected by local wildlife trusts.

Dead trees such as this beech are vital to support the ecological cycle of woodlands.

◆ MEADOW WILDLIFE ◆

The thought of a meadow in full flower conjures up clouds of butterflies, the incessant chirping of grasshoppers and crickets and dormice playing in the grass. The wildlife in a meadow can be microcosm of the living world, predator and prey, life and death.

Butterflies abound, especially the meadow brown, one of the most common butterflies in Britain. Unlike many butterfly species the female is the largest and most showy, both sexes have 'false eyes', spots on their wings to fool bird predators about the position of the correct, and more vulnerable, head area. There are other members of this 'brown' family of butterflies that cavort in meadows. The ringlet is a reclusive sort of butterfly that much prefers dark meadows with long grass. They are always found in company. Then there is the small heath, half the size of the meadow brown and much lighter brown. It delights in visiting flowers for nectar. A brown, which is actually called a white in its common name is the marbled white. It masquerades as a white since the white spots on an otherwise black butterfly show up distinctly. All these browns are highly successful in Britain's meadows since they lay their eggs on various species of grass which are, of course, common.

Sharing the meadows are skipper butterflies, which belong to a different family. They literally skip around very quickly from leaf to flower and back again. Sometimes the eye cannot perceive the movement. They also carry their wings in a unique manner, forewings up, hindwings flat when at rest. Most skippers and browns feed as caterpillars on grasses. The two most common species are the small and Essex skippers – each under $1\frac{1}{4}$in (3cm) across the wings.

Grasshoppers and crickets are in their element in grassy meadows, enjoying the three dimensional expanse of their habitat, jumping from stem to stem, stridulating like mad (that's the word for their powerful song), or munching their way through grasses or flowers as food. In a particular region of France, where crickets are so much more common than in England, there is an annual competition to find the largest number of crickets from the village meadows during a prescribed period of time. The crickets are tracked down by their chirps, captured and released after counting.

One of the most common grasshoppers in England is the meadow grasshopper which is variable in its colour, ranging from light brown to greeny-brown. Its head is all green unlike the common green grasshopper whose head is only partially green. It appears that the colour of grasshoppers is controlled by their environment and there is some evidence that demonstrates that green grasshoppers are more common than brown ones in green habitats and brown ones in brown habitats. It has also been shown that true grasshoppers actually prefer the grasses to non-grasses or herbs. A 'true grasshopper' (or acridid) is one with short antennae, rather than bush crickets (or tigonid) which have very long antennae. There are no less than twenty-one species of grasshopper and cricket in Britain and most are found amongst grasses, scrub or in gardens. One species I have commonly in my own meadow garden is the dark bush cricket. It spends most of its time sun-bathing and singing.

Life in the grassy meadow would never be complete without beetles, they seem to colonise every habitat. After all, every fifth animal on earth is a beetle. It is always satisfying to come across the bloody-nosed beetle with its six large feet and to see it demonstrate its bright red deterrent fluid which it ejects on disturbance – hence its name. Click beetles are interesting to hold in the palm of the hand to see their remarkable powers of propulsion, clicking the joint between the head and thorax, but be quick. Look out for the delightful tortoise beetles and the bright red cardinal beetle or the tiny flea beetles less than one tenth of an inch (a few millimetres) long, which spend a lot of time in company on leaves and flowers. Their hind pair of legs is modified into a muscular bulge powerful enough to propel them in a flea-like fashion over 2in (5cm). Walking through the meadow you must surely have seen the cuckoo-spit, or froth produced by a tiny true bug to protect itself.

SOME
◆ MEADOW INSECTS ◆

Common name	Latin name
Essex skipper butterfly	*Thymelicus sylvestris*
Marble white butterfly	*Melanargia galathea*
Meadow brown butterfly	*Maniola jurtina*
Ringlet butterfly	*Aphantopus hyperantus*
Small heath butterfly	*Coenonympha pamphilus*
Small skipper butterfly	*Thymelicus lineola*
Meadow grasshopper	*Chorthippus parallelus*
Common green grasshopper	*Omocestus viridulus*
Dark bush cricket	*Pholidoptera griseoaptera*
Bloody-nosed beetle	*Timarchia tenebricosa*
Tortoise beetle	*Cassida viridis*
Cardinal beetle	*Pyrochroa coccinea*

The corncrake (*Crex crex*) used to be a familiar bird of the meadows and pastures, but its decline has been alarming. Few, today have heard its characteristic rasping cry, uttered from its sanctuary in the grasses. The wilder meadows of western Eire, or the sandy grasslands (machair) of western Scotland are the places to find this intriguing species. Meadow pipits and skylarks may breed in the meadow and add to the summer weather their own cries and melodious songs.

Otters used to abound in the water meadows adjacent to the rivers and streams, the young gambolling on the slippery banks and romping through the hay. They used occasionally to be found by workmen scything the grass. Of course rabbits, hares and hazel dormice were and, in some places, still are regular visitors to the meadow, seeking refuge in the hedgerow margin.

◆ CONSERVATION MEADOWS ◆

Creating wild meadows is something that a lot of people have done in the past, and there is even more scope and variety for it today. Wildlife will integrate itself better in an untamed meadow rather than into a prim and proper one. So what are the secrets and problems?

In the grounds of his Sussex estate near East Grinstead, William Robinson, the father of wild flower gardening, created his 'alpine meadow', a rather wild affair. It was not, perhaps as one might expect today, a neat alpine 'rock' garden containing true alpine species, but a typically Robinson one. We must look at his definition of a wild garden, for in his *The Wild Garden* (1870) he is particularly keen to put the record straight 'It is applied essentially to the placing of perfectly hardy exotic plants under conditions where they will thrive without further notice.' Now, the inclusion of the word 'exotic' would surprise a lot of people. Exotic is applied to plants which are not native to Britain, sometimes also called 'introduced' or 'alien'. So the essential ingredients of his alpine meadow were in fact many bulb species from northern and southern France and Italy. These included such niceties as the delicate blue-flowered *Anemone appenina*, wood tulips (*Tulipa sylvestris*) from Touraine (Loire), grape hyacinth (*Muscari spp.*) and Spanish scilla (*Scilla spp.*). Of course, Robinson also had fritillaries and the attractive white flowers of Star of Bethlehem (*Ornithogalum umbellatum*) both more common on the continent than in England. He tried mixtures of English, Irish, Tenby and Scotch daffodils, star narcissi, wild crocuses, snowdrops and dog's tooth violets. Hardly any management of his meadow was necessary, bar an annual mowing and every spring his colourful spectacle got better and better. His only input was to plant bulbs in bold, natural groups and then leave well alone. Perhaps a lesson to us all.

You can now buy a wild flower meadow off the supermarket shelf, at least in America where 'meadows in a can' – a selection of seeds – have been on offer for some time. There is no lack of wild flower seed available from various sources in Britain either. There is a great deal of interest in growing your own wild flower meadow, a sort of DIY sow-your-own-meadow. One mixture I have seen in America is 'Birdsong Meadow', twenty species of plants to attract song birds to the garden. Europeans would recognise typical American species which do not look out of place in English herbaceous borders, coneflowers (*Rudbeckia*), Californian poppies (*Eschscholzia*), coreopsis and asters. There are also cosmos, zinnias, and wild grasses to complement this beautiful meadow selection.

English seed merchants offer a bewildering array of wild flower seed, especially from Emorsgate Seeds or John Chambers (see page 151). There are biblical plants from the 'Holy Land' comprising interesting daisies, poppies, lupins and cornflowers; seed of genuinely British native wild plants; seed mixtures taken from six annual cuttings from the famous Cricklade Meadow, and also from the Yarnton Meadow (Oxfordshire). Wild grasses and other plants for birds, butterflies and bees are all included. If these amazing selections are not enough, then there are always retail suppliers of wild flower seed which are for sale in most high streets now.

Establishment is the major headache in creating a meadow. The seed mix you buy comprises all sorts of species, which you will be looking out for soon after sowing. Some of them may not come up straight away. A lot of patience is required. The habitat into which you have sown the seeds must be just right. Details on how to prepare the soil will normally be supplied.

It is important to choose only those seed mixes which are ideal for your type of soil, acid (low pH), alkaline (higher pH), sandy or boggy. Seeds of species from one type of area will not always thrive in another set of conditions. A great deal of work is involved in preparing the ground and keeping weeds at bay until the nursery plants are established, and even then some of the species will not appear. Scientific research has shown that it takes up to 8 years after sowing to get some of the long-term perennials through to any sort of dominance or showiness in a meadow. So be really patient.

Allow the short-term perennials such as oxeye daisy to flower abundantly in the first few years, then the long-term perennials like campanulas and stinking goosefoot (*Chenopodium vulgare*) and meadow buttercup (*Ranunculus acris*) will come through. It is best to think in terms of 10 years to establish a really rich meadow from scratch, but it may look very showy and presentable after a year. As for cutting the hay and keeping down scrub encroachment, without detriment to your wild flowers, make two cuts (or grazes), one in late July, the other in late October. Your meadow will soon become the envy of all, a natural paradise and a haven for butterflies.

◆ MEADOW SURVEY ◆

If you do not want to establish an ancient meadow, or haven't the space, why not make a survey of all the fields of the parish? Take your local Ordnance Survey map (1:50,000 series, which shows one inch to the mile) and, making a rough plan of your parish, mark in all the fields.

Visit all the fields and make an observation on whether they are meadows or pastures or if they have any interesting wild flowers, in the field, around the edges, along ditches or around ponds. It might take you a long while to survey the whole parish, but it is a worthwhile job and will provide a valuable statement in time, as to the meadow potential of just one parish. Children can be involved to speed up data collection.

Another survey can be done in conjunction with, or separately from, the meadow survey. This is to assess the dominance of wild flowers in each of your most interesting meadows in the parish. Each field could be designated a rating of importance, say 1 for the 'best', down to 10 for 'poor'. The abundance of each species in all fields (you will have to tabulate your results – or use a friendly computer) can be worked out by giving a rating value, as follows: abundant, localised, frequent, occasional and rare.

◆ MOVING MEADOWS ◆

More and more frequently the press takes up the enormously popular theme of saving our valuable meadows. As demand for land grows and urban sprawl continues unabated, innocuous pieces of countryside such as flowering meadows are increasingly under threat. Supermarket chains, such as Sainsbury's and Tesco, have both become involved in big publicity exercises to save particular meadows. Local groups often arouse the awareness of the public to threatened species (frequently wild flowers like orchids or butterflies) living on these sites, and the kindly developers response has been to pay for carefully re-siting the meadow, sod by sod. Other companies have been involved too, such as English China Clay, some with the help of the government conservation body, the Nature Conservancy Council (NCC). These experiments have not been running long enough to ascertain whether they have been successful or just cosmetic. One wonders who are the winners, nature conservation and wildlife or supermarket chains? Moving meadows is one way to prolong the affected habitat and give it one more chance. Too often we see the untimely destruction of an interesting meadow before, or as, developers move in.

WOODLANDS, TREES & BOGS

• OUR VILLAGE WOODS •

It is important to understand the evolution and development of our wooded countryside in order to interpret what we have left. Our green and pleasant land is, in fact, entirely man-managed, but our association with the forest has been deep.

If we go back to 4000 B.C. the neolithic people were the first to set about cutting down the natural forests which blanketed much of Britain. The beech woods on the higher chalky ground, as on the Downs of southern England, were the first to go. Strategically this was a good place to live, looking down towards the thick oak forests of the Weald. The oak woods were gradually penetrated for the timber and food, though the going was sticky and slow.

The Saxons made inroads into the forest by establishing settlements on the banks of rivers, clearing the forest and tilling the virgin land. At places like Withyham (near Tunbridge Wells in Kent) the place name reflects the Saxon 'enclosures of willow' – withies. The water-loving willows would have grown well in the water-logged ground adjacent to the River Medway, and they still do today.

By the time the Romans arrived and Romano-British settlements were blossoming the situation looked a little different. It has been estimated that there were 70–80 Roman settlements, each not exceeding 20a (80ha) within their walls, and about 2,500 rural settlements each with an average of 300a (120ha) per settlement.

When the Normans landed and started to document their spoils, we gained an accurate measure of the state of woodlands left in the country. In 1086 only 15 per cent of England was wooded. The Norman settlements were about 2–4a (0·8–1.6ha) in size and were enclosed by original tracts of oak wood called 'shaws'. Today the word has changed its meaning and refers to a wide block of trees, hardly an original block of ancient oak wood.

Large tracts of woodland still remained, particularly in the southern and central part of Britain, where dense forest, and deep mud hindered development. Edward III (1312–77), on one of his royal 'progresses' through the Forest of the Weald (or Anderida as it was then known) had to have twenty-two guides to help him from London to Lympne on the Kentish south coast. The Forest of the Weald was about 100mi (161km) long by 40mi (64km) wide and really filled that area between the north and south Downs between Dover and Guildford.

◆ HURSTS, DENS, SPINNEYS AND SHAWS ◆

Gradually we started to reap the spoils of the forest, not only for timber and fuel, but by bringing in sheep, goats and pigs to eat the acorn bonanza. The names of so many of our villages reflect our ancient association with the forest. In Kent, especially, there are a great number of villages which end either in 'hurst' or 'den' – try looking at a local map to find place-names with a similar derivation near you.

'Hursts' – an old Teutonic word – were often wooded hilltops or knolls within the forest, from which views across the thick forest could be had and were, presumably, convenient halting stops. Typical 'hurst' names are found across southern England and north into Buckinghamshire, and include Hawkhurst, Chislehurst, Billingshurst and Amherst. Some 'hursts' were also associated with sandy areas, even sandy crossing points across rivers. Again, a glance at a local map may turn up some interesting background information.

Of 'den' villages we know a little more. Deriving from the Saxon meaning 'enclosed space' it was a living in the forest, a stockaded enclosure in which our forage animals could be confined overnight. The word is typically Kentish and at least 470 place names ending in 'den' have been recorded. Examples include Benenden, Biddenden and Marden. These 'dens' were places where people eventually settled, though at first some were just distant forage grounds for domestic animals. For instance, Tenterden was where the farmers of Thanet, 30mi (48km) away on the north-east coast of Kent, would graze their pigs; a sort of seasonal transhumance. Soon these temporary forage grounds were settled permanently.

Pannage was the all important occupation of many in each forest village. This was the right to pasture swine in the forest. The massive oak trees produced their incredible wealth of fruits which fell on to the forest floor in late summer and autumn; food for the swineherd. So housewives and boys would take their animals out through the woods, so that the pigs could scrape and snuffle up the fruits of the forest. They still do this in parts of rural Spain today. The animals were also after the pignut (*Conopodium majus*), a delicate umbellifer of the woodland floor. Its subterranean 'nut' was good for the pig as well as a bonus for youngsters. Growing by streams in damp woodlands it was easy to wash the 'nuts' in the water.

◆ POLLARDING AND COPPICING ◆

The ancient forest of Anderida was indeed a 'forest' but many people refer to it as a woodland. It would have been an oak wood. Most of the original forest disappeared, but there would have been parts which were developed without felling all the trees. Still man's management would have influenced all parts of the wood. Woodland scholars today try to find the hidden botanical clues to long lost habitats. The demise of the forest was hardly surprising since tens of thousands of woodmen were living in the woods. It is thought that just one woodman could cut down 30,000 oaks in his lifetime, which made a significant impact on the woods in the long term.

On the original forest sites, a new type of managed woodland appeared. These were coppices, to be passed down to scores of generations of villagers, as skilfully-managed, multi-role woodlands. Some of these coppices are still in use today.

The early English had a healthy respect for timber and knew how to look after it. They were great conservators since they practised woodland management which was sustainable, the operative word here, which means that they knew how to harvest trees and allow more timber to grow on for future generations. They had good reason to be prudent managers of wood for they were entirely dependent upon it. This was their natural resource, their fruit of the forest. They built timber-framed buildings – their own houses, farm buildings, village churches and glebe houses. If the clay was good and the oak grew well they might sell timbers for ship-building.

'Coppicing' and 'pollarding' were ancient crafts. Coppicing was the cutting of certain tree species at ground level, leaving them to grow on for a number of years, and then harvesting the timber again. Typical species employed for coppicing were hazel (*Corylus avellana*), hornbeam (*Carpinus betulus*) and Spanish/sweet chestnut (*Castanea sativa*). Quick-growing hazel would be cut on a cycle of 7 years, hornbeam and chestnut on fifteen. The cut stumps are known as 'stools' and persist for centuries.

Regularly treated like this the tree would keep on providing valuable timber for centuries. It was a useful woodland management technique but had to be done in the absence of grazing animals. It would have been futile to have sheep and goats grazing on the first few years' shoots, so they were always excluded. If land was limited, there was another method of management, pollarding.

Pollarding involves cutting the entire tree off at about 7ft (2m 15cm) from the ground. Many species lend themselves to this apparently drastic method and beech and oak do well. Thus two roles of timber production and understorey grazing are satisfied. In fact this is the origin of 'wood-pasture' integrating grazing with wood production. Regular pollarding of willows would supply material for basket-making or fuel,

normal oak tree profile

stag-horned oak

pollarded oak

estate oak

coppice stool oak

fallen oak

The English Oak

that of beech, hornbeam or oak for posts and fuel.

Pollarding was practised much more widely than today, and we can find plenty of examples along lanes, in hedgerows and at the corners of woods. The typical pollarded tree eventually becomes an imposing specimen with a large and sturdy trunk. Through generations of cutting the pollarded tree becomes highly distinctive, and it is precisely for this reason that certain trees were pollarded to be seen as marker or boundary trees. Hence their presence at the corners of woods and junctions of estates. Particularly fine examples of pollarded trees may be found in Epping Forest and in the New Forest thought to be 300–400 years old. Today the problem with old pollarded trees is that if regular lopping is not carried out the tree becomes very leggy, and top-heavy. It is then susceptible to toppling with high winds or burdens of snow.

It is interesting to note what William Cobbett had to say about the coppices, pollards and people working them, when he went on his journeys in East Sussex in the 1820s.

> I cannot quit Battle without observing that the country is very pretty all about it . . . It was rainy as I came home; but the woodmen were at work. A great many *hop-poles* [pole for supporting the stalk of the hop] are cut here, which makes the coppices more valuable than in many other parts. The women work in the coppices, shaving the bark of the hop-poles, and, indeed, at various others parts of the business. These poles are shaved to prevent *maggots* from breeding in the bark and accelerating the destruction of the pole.

Whilst Cobbett is travelling in Suffolk he notes:

> Almost every bank of every field is studded with *pollards*, that is to say, trees that have been *beheaded*, at from six to twelve feet [1·8–3.6m] from the ground than which nothing in nature can be more ugly. These pollards become very hollow very soon and, as timber, are fit for nothing but gate-posts, even before they are hollow.

Times have changed somewhat since Cobbett galloped around the country casting his critical eye on the welfare of the nation. The coppice woodlands have suffered greatly. Since the beginning of this century, coppicing has become generally non-viable economically and coppice woodlands have either been grubbed out or left. This has resulted, fortuitously, in the evolution of a slightly different habitat, from wildlife's point of view, the 'neglected coppice woodland'. Such wild coppices have benefited some woodland insects and birds particularly. Previously coppices were either entirely given over to coppice production, or, grown with standard trees (trees grown alone without support), such as oaks or pines for more sturdy building timber. This creates the 'coppice with standards' habitat, many of which are in nature conservation hands today. We meet the same sort of arrangement in the 'hedgerow with standards' in the next chapter (pages 52–75).

The East Sussex woods that Cobbett found so thick and mossy are still important places for wildlife. None is so typical as Forewood at Battle, which is one of the Royal Society for the Protection of Birds' (RSPB's) best woodland reserves. It is a neglected coppice woodland which sports many species including the nightingale (*Luscinia mergarhynchos*). Studies carried out in other coppice woods in Kent, have shown that these migrant birds have a preference for coppice woodland of a particular thickness. In a chestnut coppice they prefer stands between 5–10 years old. At 15 years the stands are too dense (and usually they are felled at this time), and in years 1–5 the stands are too thin. The male nightingale is a trifle fickle. To be heard and not seen is his motto. He has to seek the particular density of vegetation in which to take up station and proclaim his presence, without being seen. He now prefers a man-made habitat which is interesting. Whatever did he do before? Perhaps he liked blackthorn thickets before coppice was invented.

There is a species of butterfly which is associated with neglected coppice woodlands and that is the white admiral (*Lagoda camilla*). It is the logo of the Sussex Wildlife Trust (not surprising since East Sussex is the most wooded county in England, and this is a treasured woodland species). Thanks to neglected coppice woodlands abounding in East Sussex, to the tune of some 32 per cent of all the ancient woods, the butterfly has prospered. It is, however, the success of the caterpillar food plant, honeysuckle (*Lonicera periclymenum*) which has allowed the species to flourish. The downfall of one of man's habitats has given new hope to at least one beautiful species. An unsung, butterfly success story.

The early Britons were skilled with coppicing hazel (*Corylus avellana*). It grows as a native in Britain and lends itself to being bent over and pinned or layered to the ground. In this way, new plants could be 'struck' easily. A rapid grower, hazel would soon, after 7 years, produce shoots big enough to be cut. The pliable stems were ideal for making wattles and hurdles.

Sheep had to be stockaded in the open country (like the Downs or Chilterns) and penned for the night. The movable hurdles were ideal barriers, lightweight and easily erected. This was the time when there were more sheep in the country than people. Each hurdle was a rectangular frame interwoven with withes of hazel or willow, and as such, was called a wattle. Today a great number of traditional hazel coppice woods are still extant, though many are neglected.

Another woodland type that we see a lot of in the British countryside is the chestnut coppice woodland. This is sweet chestnut, otherwise called Spanish chestnut which gives us a clue to its origins. It is an introduced species from the Mediterranean which, it is thought, arrived with the Romans who taught us how to coppice it. Again, numerous such chestnut coppice woodlands are still in existence today. Many may be several hundred years old, because the old system of managing the woods persisted until at least the beginning of this century. Neglected chestnut coppice woodland is all too frequent a sight. Oliver Rackham, the author of some fine books on woodland history has recorded one sweet chestnut 'stool' 16ft (4m 90cm) across at Holbrooke Park (East Suffolk) which is thought to be not later than the Middle Ages. Of ash stools Rackham knew of a 18½ft (5m 60cm) one in Felsham Hall Wood (West Sussex) thought to be at least 1,000 years old.

• OAK FOR SHIPS AND HOUSES •

Boat-building and house-building consumed a vast amount of the Forest of the Weald. This was hardly surprising since we had exploited the timber as if it were an inexhaustible resource.

Henry VII (1491–1547) became a little concerned about the supply of timber for boats running out in the Weald and changed his running operations from the Cinque Ports to the more wooded Portsmouth in anticipation. He made a statute in 1544 which required parishes to keep a dozen standard trees in every acre of woodland felled. It would be good to see this statute re-enacted today, a small sacrifice when planning officers give the approval to developers for woodland clearance.

In 1580 the future supply of oak was still causing some concern. Elizabeth I did try to stop charcoal burning in the environs of the Thames but woodland clearance continued unabated. Charcoal is still, incidentally, carried on as a traditional woodland craft in the village of Seddlescombe (East Sussex). There the wood smoke hangs thickly over the woods and in the lanes, presumably as it always used to do.

The numbers of oak trees felled to make boats and timber-framed buildings was amazing. There were parts of the forest relatively rich in fine oaks which could be plundered. In Elizabethan times it is thought (by the National Trust) that 3,000 fully grown oak trees (or 900a/360ha of oak wood) would have been required to make a single three-decker battleship. Quite an undertaking for a vessel that might only last one year. It was estimated by another authority that to build one of Nelson's ships would have required 1,000 prime oak trees from the forest. This

◆ ECOLOGICAL AREA ◆

1. Canopy   The crown of the tree is used as an assembly area for butterflies, such as the purple emperor (*Apatura iris*) or for the swirling masses of long-horned moths (*Adela*). The canopy of an English oak wood has not been studied intensively by naturalists.

2. Buds   Sticky buds which develop in the spring provide food for small insects and are the site for egg-laying in the purple hairstreak butterfly (*Quercusia quercus*).

3. Catkins   Oak trees have individual male and female flowers, and in the male catkins various tiny wasps (cynipids) and weevil beetles live.

4. Acorns   Internal feeders are the caterpillars of the tortricid moth (*Cydia splendana*). Ninety-seven per cent of acorns are food for insects, small mammals, squirrels and jays.

5. Leaves   Can be defoliated by many sorts of insect larvae and weevil beetles. The oak tortrix moth (*Tortrix viridana*) can be so invasive in the spring that all the oak leaves of a mighty oak are defoliated. The tree grows another set without any problem.

6. Twigs   Eggs of winter moths (*Operophtera brumata*) remain on twigs over winter and the larvae of sawflies bore into the twigs.

7. Trunk   Camouflaged moths like the peppered moth (*Biston betularia*) take advantage of the rough surface to conceal themselves during the day. Lichens use the trunk as a valuable mini-habitat.

8. Branches   Another refuge for lichens.

9. Rot-holes   Rot holes develop where a limb is lost and water cannot soak away. They are dangerous for the tree as a source of infection, but valuable as breeding sites for mosquitoes and watering holes for birds.

10. Macrofungi   Signs of internal fungal disease within the tree, these bracket fungi are simply reproductive units designed to disperse spores. They are also used as a substrate for breeding flies.

11. Deadwood   The oak will always produce branches of dead wood below as the upper branches prosper. The more dead wood on the tree that falls on the ground, the more wood-boring beetles one can expect in an area.

12. Roots   Out of sight, tree roots are widely colonised by fungi which often given vital nutrients to the plant in return for 'board and lodgings' – a symbiotic relationship where both partners benefit.

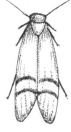

Long-horned moth

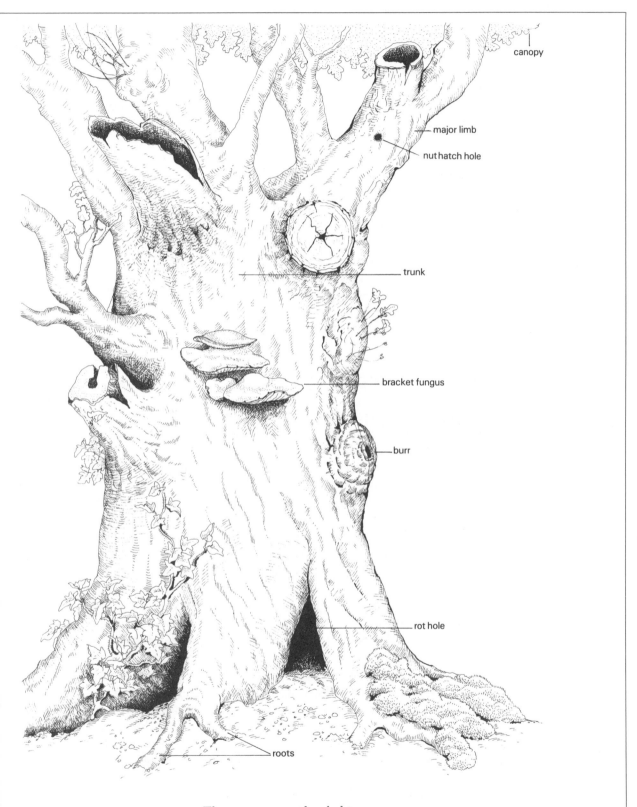

canopy

major limb

nut hatch hole

trunk

bracket fungus

burr

rot hole

roots

The tree as a complete habitat

would have represented about 60a (24ha) of forest if that forest had a density of 12–20 oaks per acre (0·4ha). Quite an operation. Getting the wood to the docks was an onerous task through the famous Wealden clay, which was supposed to have swallowed up whole wagons in its sticky mud. Some timbers took two years to haul from Tonbridge to Chatham Dockyard, a distance of only 20mi (8km) but over the North Downs.

Wooden houses used a colossal number of prime forest oaks. Most of the thousands of timber-framed buildings of the Weald were constructed during the sixteenth century, either from newly-cut wood or from old ships' timbers. Wattle and daub, often using willow as an ingredient, was used to fill up between the timber sections. Black poplar (*Populus nigra*), now sadly a very rare species in our landscape often supplied the 's' shaped cruck joints to hold up the roof. Large numbers of small oaks were used to make typical medieval buildings and the trees could be coppiced every 30–80 years to assure a renewable supply. The houses were frequently aligned north-east to south-west to maximise on the warming effect of the morning and evening sun.

◆ THE OAK ◆

Our rural heritage is associated more with the oak than any other tree in Britain. With the plethora of oaks on village greens, Royal Oak pubs and old customs like Oak Apple Day, the oak is truly British.

The most common oak species is called the English oak but it is also known as the common oak or pedunculate oak (*Quercus robur*). Its peduncle is a glorified name for the stalk which carries the acorn or nut. This distinguishes it from the sessile oak (*Quercus petraea*) whose acorns are born stalkless on the twigs. English oaks are found more often on clayey ground, rather than the sessile oak which prefers drier ground. The sessile is the taller of the two species and is found further to the west than its relation.

With spreading branches, the English oak can grow to a venerable old age. Torn by storms, it seems to survive several centuries. There are innumerable famous oaks up and down the country, indeed one recorder noted over 130 such named oaks. Elizabeth I is associated with several royal oaks, under which, or in which, she hid. There is the famous hollow oak in Greenwich Park which was used as a temporary lock-up for park offenders, and another on the village green at Northiam under which Elizabeth I once changed her shoes, en route for the coast. The Boscobel Oak is associated with Charles II (1630–85) who hid in it to escape his persecutors, thus the Oak Apple Day, which is 24 May in celebration of his successful flight from danger. There is a Robin Hood and a Wilberforce Oak as well as a Nell Gwyn oak. As Rudyard Kipling said 'Huge oaks and old, the which we hold'.

Above left English woodlands being coppiced. *Above right* Afforestation continues to ruin our countryside. *Below* These oak woods around the CEGB sub-station at Ninfield, East Sussex are now maintained as a nature reserve.

·OAK WILDLIFE·

Oak is accredited with the richest fauna of any tree in Britain. This is a reflection of its long association with the countryside. The longer a species has been in existence in any country the more species of insect it has associated with it. This is now a well proven biological principle. English oak has over 280 species of insect either partially or completely dependent upon it. Not all species will be found on any one oak, but this is the total number of insect species found nationwide in a big survey. In comparison, spruce has less than forty and you might expect monkey puzzle trees to have even fewer. Over 300 species of lichen have also been found in association with oaks throughout Britain, signifying a long association.

The English oak can withstand a veritable barrage of insect depredation. In mid-June there are known to be 110 species of butterfly and moth which are associated with it. By mid-August this has tailed off to sixty-five species. The reason is the chemical defence built up in the leaves; namely tannin, that ingredient of tea, which hungry caterpillars do not like.

The English oak tree can actually be divided into a dozen ecological areas, each providing an opportunity for difference forms of wildlife from owls to woodlice.

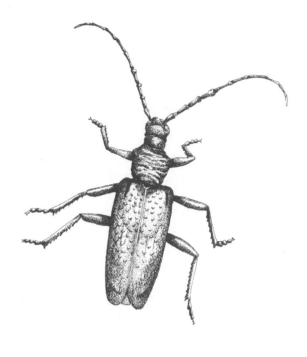

Longhorn beetle

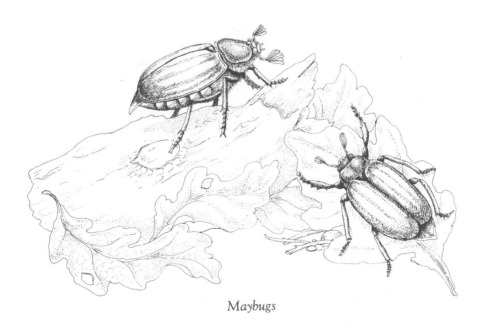

Maybugs

Above Along the green roads which cut across the Burren's limestone pavement (W. Eire), wild flowers prosper.
Below Some elms had injections to prevent Dutch elm disease, but all was in vain.

• AGEING TREES •

The girth of any tree, including an oak, will give some idea of its antiquity. Very roughly a tree growing by itself in the open, in good soil will put on 1in (2.5cm) of girth every year. One in a wood or hedgerow will put on ½in (1.2cm). Waterlogging and poor soils will stunt the growth of a tree and local situations must be taken into consideration. Always take girth measurements of trees at about a yard from the ground for conformity of records for comparative purposes.

Conifers grow at much quicker rates and they are easier to age. Simply look up the trunk and count the number of levels from which whorls of branches originate. A new set is produced every year. Try it out on your next Christmas tree, a Norwegian spruce.

• ANCIENT WOODLANDS •

The concept of ancient woodlands is a very emotive subject. So what are they, how do you recognise them in your parish, and how ancient is ancient?

Quite simply ancient woodlands are woods which have been growing as woods on original woodland sites. Barring a few decades of wood clearance when the trees of the original forest were felled, we are talking about woods which have been traditionally managed on the site for centuries. It is thought that English oak has the potential to live to 2,000 years in Britain, beech and lime to 1,000 years, though a figure of 500 years for an oak is more appropriate considering storm damage.

A better term for an ancient woodland could actually be 'semi-natural woodland', since this describes the type of wood we are dealing with. Secondary woods are those that grow on cleared land, as opposed to primary woodland which is the original type of woodland. It is also important to be aware of the term 'climax community' since it is a scientific term which denotes the ultimate habitat which will develop on a given type of soil. In this context, an original (primary or primeval) woodland would be a climax community. A further term to handle is 'relic', and this is loosely used for an original woodland or an ancient woodland. So take your choice.

You have to have a keen eye to detect ancient woodlands. The presence of certain flowering plants, ferns and mosses is indicative of ancient woodlands, but you need to be a competent botanist. The presence of certain birds also helps. You don't have to be a terribly competent ornithologist to identify 'indicator' species, as they are all called. You can also get a feel for an ancient woodland by the amount of rotting timber on the woodland floor. To make a serious appraisal of the ancient woodlands of your parish the quickest method is to consult old maps. This method relies upon some sound facts.

One third to one half of the remaining 15 per cent of England's woods which were present in 1086 (Domesday Book), were unceremoniously removed during the twelfth and thirteenth centuries in a period of insatiable demand for timber. Those woods which remained, and stayed intact until the beginning of the fourteenth century, were most likely to remain intact for the next 500 years. Bearing in mind that 50 per cent of ancient woodlands have been lost during 1945–75 (approximately equalling the whole woodland destruction over the last 400 years!), what we have left are ancient woodlands. This means about 609,756–731,707a (243,902–292,682ha) of ancient wood which should always be conserved and never destroyed.

By comparing the woods which were present on old maps, with present day ones, the woods which are still with us today are highly likely to be the ancient ones. However, this does not pick up small woods and shaws which are likely to have been missed off the earlier maps.

The old Ordnance Survey (OS) maps of 1815, (one inch to the mile), are excellent places to start your detective work. This series has been reprinted in recent years by David & Charles, Publishers. The maps show accurate outlines of woods. The OS 1:10,000 (or six inches to the mile) maps give even more details such as boundaries, individual trees (often pollards as boundary markers), and clues from local place names. These maps can be consulted in public libraries alongside old estate and parish records for further information.

To give some idea of the abundance of ancient woods in an area, it is worth looking at the distribution of ancient woods in East Sussex. This is the largest wooded county in England with more of its wooded heritage to collate and protect than most counties. Map studies carried out by the Wealden District Council in 1980 showed scores of ancient woodlands throughout most of the northern part of the Wealden district. Of these, 32 per cent were broad-leaved, the rest converted to coniferous or mixed plantations. East Sussex's ancient broad-leaved woodlands comprise typical coppice with standards, often with horn-beam, which reflects the traditional iron smelting of the Weald. Hornbeam was a slow burner which gave out a lot of heat.

Around the country there are numerous examples of ancient woodlands. Prime examples are Rushbeds Wood, part of Bernwood Forest (Oxfordshire), thought to be 7,000 years old and unmixed. It was purchased for £52,000 in 1983 and supports nearly 200 species of flowering plant, and 33 species of woodland butterfly. It is one of the leading butterfly haunts in England.

To the east there is the best example of an ancient wood on East Anglia's boulder clay, Bradfield Woods (Suffolk). It is thought to have been coppiced traditionally since the twelfth century. Today it is still managed in the old manner, but by men with modern equipment such as chain saws and tractors. Each woodman will cut about 10a (4ha) over the winter. The flora of this wood is richer than any other in Eastern England.

The richest and most diverse woodland in southern England is claimed to be Boulsbury Wood (Dorset). There are plenty of others, like Lime Breach Wood (Avon) and Ebernoe Common (West Sussex) most of which are fine botanical places and designated SSSIs (see page 141). Wistman's Wood (Devon) on the south side of Dartmoor is a particular favourite, a stunted and gnarled oak wood growing from massive boulders. It belongs to the Duchy of Cornwall. All too frequently these SSSI ancient woods are threatened by development, clear-felling or quarrying, as was Asham Wood (Somerset) in 1984.

◆ INDICATOR SPECIES ◆

Indicator species are simply those plants or animals which give an indication of an ancient habitat. By themselves they are not necessarily indicative of an old site, together with others, they are.

Much ado has been made about dog's mercury (*Mercurialis perennis*), sometimes a little out of context. Even *The Times* devoted a column to this indicative species, but the reality is that there are well over 100 indicator species that can help us put a longevity tag on a wood. It is true that the presence of 'mercury' is a useful guide but it must be viewed alongside other species.

Not surprisingly, because of the diverse nature of British woodland, the tree experts of this country have divided our woodlands into thirty-two types according to their indicative flora. The basis of their division is the quality of the soil, whether it is relatively wet or dry, acid or alkaline. These types of woodland can be broken down into four major groups, (i) neutral-alkaline in English lowland, (ii) acid-neutral in south-west England and north-east England, (iii) strongly acidic and light soils of uplands and lowlands and (iv) strongly acidic and peaty soils of Scotland, Wales and north England. These are the results from thorough surveys which, incredibly, collected information from $1,648 \times 220yd^2$ ($200m^2$) samples from 103 woods of the 2,500-odd British woods.

◆ FALLEN TIMBER ◆

Fallen timber is one of the most important parts of any woodland. If we could walk in the footsteps of early explorers penetrating woods for the first time, we could find our way barred by tons of old wood. Up to a third of the wood may comprise dead or dying wood, as was found in the mainly coniferous Swiss National Forest which has 20 million trees. Careful studies in a virgin forest of firs and spruces in Colorado (USA),

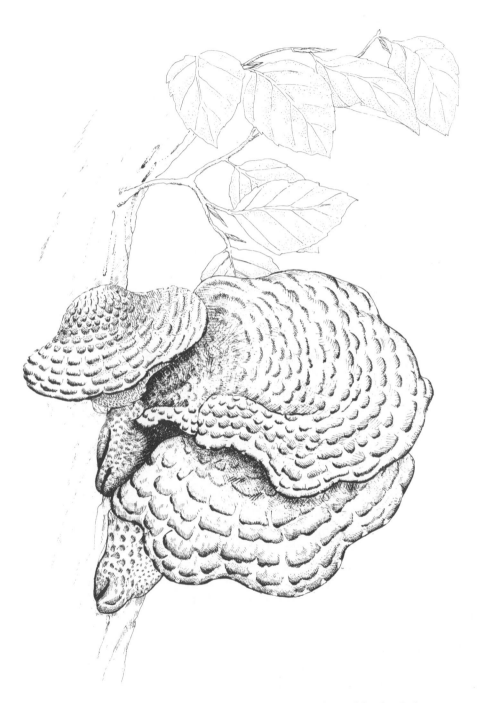

Damp woodlands encourage fungi, like this Polyporus squamosus *which in turn aids decomposition.*

showed that there were approximately 8.7 blown-down tree trunks in every 110yd^2 (100m^2).

This high amount of old wood is vital for supporting the ecological cycles of woodlands. Death and decay is essential for recycling nutrients. Damp woodlands encourage fungi which aid decomposition. In temperate woodlands the recycling process is much slower than tropical rain forests where the increased temperature enhances decay. Apart from fungi and bacteria, the decomposing process is aided by thousands of wood-boring insects which live in or on the old wood and in the decaying leaf litter.

Decay progresses in a series of overlapping stages. Insects and fungi loosen up the wood, which then become home to all sorts of invertebrates, like woodlice, nematodes and spiders. Birds move in to eat invertebrates (which includes insects) and nest in the old wood. Twenty British bird species nest in old wood.

The extent of insect involvement in wood decay is profound. If the extensive ecological surveys of Wytham Woods are anything to go by, this single typical wood contains about one sixth to one fifth of the entire British fauna. This means over 5,000 species of animals (mostly insects) from the 25,000–30,000 animals in Britain.

The importance of Wytham Woods in Oxfordshire is that it is a wood which has been subjected to continuous ecological surveys by generations of learned professors and students from Oxford University over decades. It is about 1,000a (400ha) and represents about 1/250,000th the size of England. Rather more is known about this wood than any other in England.

There is every good reason for leaving fallen timber, but in the right place. Those people with large amounts of fallen timber as a result of the hurricane of 16 October, 1987, take note.

There is no need to leave fallen timber in the open. It will only become 'heat-sterilised'. Continued fluctuations in temperature as the sun heats the wood during the day and cools it at night is not conducive to insects responsible for decay. The wood essentially becomes a living fossil and will remain in that state for decades, decomposition progressing incredibly slowly. It is much better to drag the wood to a shady hedgerow, where temperatures remain fairly constant and the log keeps moist. There are exceptions, elder will dry off in the open, but keeps a soft-centre, ideal for some insects. It also follows that dead trees standing in the open will heat-sterilise and should be cut down, and the wood piled in the corner of a field, save for elm, which should be burnt on site to limit the spread of elm-bark beetles.

Over 1,000 insect species are known from wood bark, and about half of them have been recorded at some time in Wytham Wood. At Wytham, 456 insect species were known to John Elton in his classic *The Patterns of Animal Communities* published in 1966 (recommended reading). Over 500 species found elsewhere in Britain live in the same sort of woodland habitat. The usefulness of wood-boring insects is that it opens up wood for the penetration of fungi to aid in decomposition.

Think twice about removing dead and dying wood, since you will deplete the ecology of your woodland or glade by at least 20 per cent of its fauna.

◆ TREE PLANTING ◆

Many people are faced with the problem of tree replacement. Trees all too frequently blow down, split or are killed by fungi. So what can you do? If you have to take a tree down always think of replacing it with another. There is an even greater reason to plant trees; there are too many old trees in the country and not enough young ones to replace them. The ratio between old trees and young ones is far too high (1:3). We must plant to redress the balance.

First of all try to generate new material from the original tree. Take a woody shoot or small branch and strike it in the ground. This is more likely to 'take' if it is done in the autumn. Alternatively save some fruits and seeds and try to grow them on.

If you have a *carte blanche* for planting up an old orchard or field, then think seriously about planting native trees. These are supremely capable of coping with the British climate, and there are about 32 species to choose from. Take note of the type of soil you have. Is it acid or alkaline, sandy or boggy? Natives are very particular about what sort of soil they grow in, so consult the lists, or better still, see which native trees are doing best in your own locality. Choose these.

Dog rose

• NATIVE •
BRITISH TREES

English name	Latin name
Alder	Alnus glutinosa
Apple, Crab	Malus sylvestris
Ash	Fraxinus excelsior
Aspen	Populus tremula
Beech	Fagus sylvatica
Birch, Downy	Betula pubescens
Birch, Silver	Betula pendula
Cherry, Bird	Prunus padus
Cherry, Wild; Gean	Prunus avium
Elder	Sambucus edulis
Elm, Wych	Ulmus glabra
Elm, English	Ulmus procera
Hazel	Corylus avellana
Hawthorn	Crataegus monogyna
Hawthorn, Midland	Crataegus aevigata
Holly	Ilex aquifolium
Hornbeam	Carpinus betulus
Lime, Small-leaved	Tilia cordata
Lime, Large-leaved	Tilia platyphyllos
Maple, Common or Field	Acer campestre
Oak, Common	Quercus robur
Oak, Sessile	Quercus petraea
Poplar, Black	Populus nigra
Rowan, Mountain Ash	Sorbus aucuparia
Scots pine	Pinus sylvestris
Sloe, Blackthorn	Prunus spinosa
Whitebeam	Sorbus aria
Wild service	Sorbus torminalis
Willow, Crack	Salix fragilis
Willow, Goat	Salix caprea
Willow, Grey	Salix cinerea
Yew	Taxus baccata

• NATIVE •
BRITISH SHRUBS

English name	Latin name
Birch, Dwarf	Betula nana
Blackberry	Rubus fruticosus
Box	Buxus sempervirens
Broom	Sarothamnus scoparius
Buckthorn	Rhamnus catharticus
Buckthorn, Alder	Frangula alnus
Buckthorn, Sea	Hippophae rhamnoides
Cranberry	Vaccinium oxycoccus
Cowberry	Vaccinium vitis-idaea
Crowberry	Empetrum nigrum
Dog rose	Rosa canina
Dogwood	Cornus sanguinea
Gorse	Ulex europaeus
Gorse, Western	Ulex galli
Guelder rose	Viburnum opulus
Honeysuckle	Lonicera periclymenum
Juniper	Juniperus communis
Mistletoe	Viscum album
Privet	Ligustrum vulgare
Raspberry	Rubus idaeus
Spindle	Euonymus europaeus
Sweetgale	Myrica gale
Traveller's joy (old man's beard, wild clematis)	Clematis vitalba
Wayfaring tree	Viburnum lantana
Willow	(at least 10 species)

Honeysuckle

Some natives like field maple provide stunning autumn colours, equal to many introduced maples from North America. Aspen, birches, willows and poplars are good for encouraging insects. Alder, cherry, oaks, rowan and wild service trees are good for birds. If you want to plant tree species which are rare in the wild, then go for the wild service tree, black poplar (not Lombardy poplar which is a variety), small-leaved lime and wych elm. If you have a wet corner to plant up use alder and willows. Native trees (and shrubs) attract far more wildlife than introduced trees (and shrubs). On chalk choose beech, not oak. On clay choose oak, not beech.

There is no doubt that by planting native trees, you will produce a full-balanced and fully-integrated ecological system on your own doorstep.

If, however, you favour introduced species, then you have more possibilities. You gain colour, different tree profiles, quick-growing trees, and you lose wildlife appeal and, often, any natural resistance to the British climate. If may be that you have lost some fine specimen trees and wish to propagate from these. Why not, there are some wonderful examples like the tulip tree (*Liriodendron tulipifera*), which offers exciting yellow hues in autumn, or the taller, quick-growing redwoods (*Sequoiadendron* spp.) from California with their spongy, fire-resistant bark. They take from cuttings.

The other quick-growing conifers like *Cupressus macrocarpa* do not add much to an English garden. A park or municipal arboretum is fine for them, but they look out of place in a garden. As a screen to block off neighbours, they have a short-term role but they grow in an ungainly fashion into normal forest trees and have little aesthetic or wildlife appeal.

A word must be said about 'forest trees'. This is a term which applies to many native and introduced species. They literally grow to forest height. Where they occur in the wild they exist as forests or woods. Typically, an English oak wood has a canopy about 40–50ft (12–15m) high. Some conifers reach 60–80ft (18–24m). Remember this when you are planting. It may not be your problem in 80 years time when the trees you plant reach maturity, but they will take up a huge space, may undermine walls and pavements with their roots, shade out smaller shrubs and produce large quantities of leaf litter – sometimes unwanted by neighbours. All these points must be taken into consideration when planning the position of trees.

One forestry technique is to plant young trees close together, seemingly too close together. Though it looks as if one is wasting time and money by planting the trees like this, there is a good reason. It has been shown that sapling trees in company actually protect each other; they all grow better than those trees exposed to the elements by themselves. Unlike the municipal authorities we do not always have the finances to plant masses of trees, but if you do have the chance, consider

• ACROSTICS •

Acrostics are word puzzles. There has never been a better time to plant trees, especially in the south and east. Why not baffle people in the 21st century by planting an acrostic. Don't wait until an Arbor Day or a National Tree Week. Get started now.

Use the first letter of each tree to spell out a motto, saying or quotation. Try to stick to all common names, or all Latin names of trees (it's not easy), and do leave documentary evidence of your plantings. The village green is a better place for planting than along the high street.

Some parishes, like Eynsford (Darenth Valley, north-west Kent) tried this last century. They planted 'My son, be wise' (Proverbs Ch. 27, v. 11) on the Diamond Jubilee of Queen Victoria (using **Maple, Yew, Sycamore, Oak, Negundo, Birch, Elm, Weigela, Ivy, Sumach, Elder**). They also planted, ambitiously, 'Who keeps one end in view, makes all things serve' (from Browning), and 'The best is yet to be, the last of life for which the first was made', and very appropriately 'Be prepared', round the scout hut.

Why not have a go yourself. The possibilities are endless.

'Jerusalem' could be **Judas tree, Elm, Rowan, Umbrella magnolia, Strawberry tree, Alder, Lime, Elm** and **Magnolia**.

Two separate plantings are suggested for 'More trees please' using common names or Latin names. Only the genus is given; you can choose the species you like, or make different selections to suit your soil, aspect, local climate and availability of species. As there are so many oak species (over 65) to choose from, why not have oaks for the Latin 'O's which are more difficult to find?

◆ ACROSTIC for 'More Trees Please'

LETTER	ALTERNATIVE 1. Using English names	ALTERNATIVE 2. Using Latin names
M	Maple	Morus
O	Osier	Olearia
R	Rowan	Robinia
E	Elm	Eucalyptus
T	Tulip tree	Tsuga
R	Redwood	Rhamnus
E	Elm	Eucalyptus
E	Elm	Eucalyptus
S	Service tree	Sorbus
P	Poplar	Picea
L	Lime	Liriodendron
E	Elm	Eucalyptus
A	Almond	Acer
S	Scots pine	Salix
E	Elm	Euonymus

close planting, with a view to taking out the worst trees in years to come.

Another tip is to buy translucent plastic guards which enclose the first 2ft (0.6m) of the stem and protect against grazing rabbits and against mowers and strimmers.

Small nursery trees are relatively cheap to buy. They range from tiny 'whips' to ones just over 3ft (1m) or so high. In urban areas choose pollution-tolerant trees.

POLLUTION-TOLERANT &
· POLLUTION-SENSITIVE TREES ·

POLLUTION-TOLERANT

English name	Latin name
Acacia, False	Robinia pseudoacacia
Beech, Common, European	Fagus sylvatica
Cedar, Western Red	Thuja plicata
Cypress, Lawson	Chaemocyparis lawsoniana
Maple, Field	Acer campestre
Oak, Common, English	Quercus robur
Plane, London	Platanus × orientalis
Sycamore	Acer pseudoplatanus
Yew	Taxus baccata

POLLUTION-SENSITIVE

English name	Latin name
Alder, Grey	Alnus incana
Ash	Fraxinus excelsior
Birch, Silver	Betula pendula
Cedar, Atlantic	Cedrus atlantica
Larch, European	Larix decidua
Pine, Scots	Pinus sylvestris
Pine, Weymouth	Pinus strobus
Spruce, Norway	Picea abies
Walnut, Common	Juglans regia

The hole to receive the new tree should be twice as big as the root ball. Fit the hole to the tree, rather than the tree to the hole. Drive a sturdy stake into the hole. The base of the hole should then be pricked over generously to allow for drainage (you can always put some clinker or broken bricks at the base), scatter a handful of a proprietary tree dressing (optional) over the bottom, and then plant the tree. In drought areas make sure there is a depression in the soil around the stem so that water does not drain away from the plant. Tie the stem of the tree to the post with a good tree-tie, which automatically allows for growth without constriction. After-care is as important as site preparation, so check your trees after storms and high winds.

◆ FORESTRY – THE INIMICAL THREAT ◆

Take note, we are so often beguiled by figures. The woodlands that are the dearest to our hearts are oak woods or beech woods, the original woods of the land. Yet we are bombarded with figures which tell of enormous expansion of British woodlands. All would seem to be rosy. Lots more woods being established. What the figures don't always indicate is that they are the wrong sort for wildlife and landscape. The deciduous woodlands that Elizabethan England depended upon are not wanted today. They are just not economic. Governments (of any hue) are not likely to protect forest wildlife at the expense of growing their sort of forestry trees.

The Forestry Commission was set up in 1919 to reduce our dependence on imported wood. Has it worked? Judge for yourselves. Seventy years later we are still 90 per cent dependent upon imported timber. The price we have paid is afforestation of the highlands, lowlands and heathlands. There is a colossal expansion of forestry plantations expected into the next century. Do we really want it? And at what price the landscape and wildlife!

Do not be fooled. Man-made coniferous woods are really boring places for wildlife compared to the habitats they replaced. Our land has been taken from us, the ancient meadows, woods and heathlands in particular. Much of our rural heritage has gone.

Native coniferous woods on the other hand, like the ancient Caledonian pine forest in Western Scotland, are remarkably interesting places with pine martens (*Martes martes*) and capercaille (*Tetrao urogallus*). It was good news in early 1987 to learn that the Royal Society for the Protection of Birds (RSPB) acquired a large slice of this important natural habitat – some 4,000a (1,600ha) of the 30a^2 (48ha^2) of the Abernethy estate. It is adjacent to two other important RSPB sites, Loch Garten with its famous ospreys (*Panion haliaetus*) and the Upper Glen Avon, bringing the total under conservation to 30,000a (12,000ha); a major coup for a voluntary conservation body.

The tragic and irreversible destruction of some of Britain's natural habitats was finally acknowledged by the Nature Conservancy Council (NCC) in 1987 with the publication of their hard-hitting *Birds, Bogs & Forestry*. This is the first time that the NCC, as official upholders of nature conservation in Britain, have been bold enough to say that afforestation has been ruining our precious countryside. Ninety-four per cent of Britain's peatlands have been lost since the middle of last century, half of it since 1945. It is a grave position, since if current trends persist, the natural resource will be entirely gone in 30 years time. Yes, resource is what it is, though some people do not think of it that way.

The effects of forestry are particularly well seen in the Flow Country of northern Scotland. This is a 1,500mi^2 (2,400km^2) area comprising the districts of Caithness and Sutherland. It is the largest primeval blanket bog in Britain and represents one tenth of the world's blanket bog. It is possibly the largest single expanse of blanket bog in the world.

Forestry in the Flow Country caught us all by surprise in the 1980s. The wonderful bogs have been systematically exploited by the Forestry Commission and a private company acting on behalf of a small number of wealthy clients. Unfortunately, prime wildlife refuges have been ploughed up with special double ploughs able to cross the tiny pools which make up much of the area. Sitka spruce and lodgepole pine have been established in their place. The futility of the venture is that just a handful of people gained tax advantages from doing this, at the price everyone else has to pay for loss of irreplaceable prime habitat. In the House of Commons it was reported that British tax-payers were paying £30 million each year to subsidise private forestry investments; £100 per acre incentives for planting conifers. There was public outcry in late 1987. Geoffrey Lean of *The Observer* wrote a brilliant exposé of the levels to which forestry tax incentives had permeated society. The incentives were stopped in early 1988.

The Flow Country of Caithness and Sutherland is important to Britain as a breeding area for birds. In decreasing order of importance, the following birds breed there. The figures in brackets indicate the percentage of the British population which breed in the area. Greenshank (*Tringa nebularia*) (66 per cent), greylag goose (*Anser anser*) (43 per cent), dunlin (*Calidris alpina*) (39 per cent), black-throated diver (*Gavia arctica*) (20 per cent), wigeon (*Anas penelope*) (20 per cent), golden plover (*Pluvialis apricaria*) (18 per cent).

It is incumbent upon Britain to protect these important habitats and threatened wildlife. In fact it has given its obligation to do so by accepting international commitment. There are four commitments.

The first is Annex I of the European communities Directive on the Conservation of Wild Birds (1979). Here, member states (including Britain) have agreed to take special steps to protect important birds and their habitats. Many of the Flow Country birds are formally listed in Annex I.

Second, the birds' habitats are covered by the Berne Convention that 'national policies for the conservation of wild flora, wild fauna and natural habitats, with particular attention to endangered and vulnerable species . . . and endangered species' should be drawn up, was ratified by the International Union for the Conservation of Nature (IUCN), the World Wide Fund for Nature (WWF) and the United Nations Environment Programme (UNEP) in 1980, by the NCC in 1986 and the Council for the Protection of Rural England (CPRE) in 1987, among others.

Third, the peatlands are covered under the Ramsar agreement signed by Britain in 1973 and ratified in 1976. All parties agreed that wetlands constituted a resource of great economic, cultural, scientific and recreational value, and that their loss would be irreparable.

Fourth, the World Heritage Convention (ratified by Britain in 1984) stressed the importance of conserving those outstanding natural features which are regarded as universally important to mankind. The International Union for the Conservation of Nature (IUCN) have called for the peatlands of Caithness and Sutherland to be declared a World Heritage Site because of their key importance for wildlife.

It gives a faint glimmer of hope that the recent cessation of tax advantages will in some way show that the government is trying to redress the balance. Unfortunately, so much damage has already been done that any attempts at re-establishment of habitat would be unsuccessful. In the words of the government's conservation body, the NCC, 'afforestation is inimical to the survival of moorland birds'. They conclude that the loss of the peatlands of Caithness and Sutherland represent perhaps the most massive single loss of important wildlife habitats since the last war. Most of this has been since the Wildlife & Countryside Act of 1981. They say that any subsequent losses will be done through deliberate decisions in full knowledge of the facts to date.

About 130 pairs of greenshank have already been lost from the Flow Country due to forestry. Approximately 630 pairs of the British population used to breed there each year. Both black-throated divers and red-throated divers (*Gavia stellata*) are inconvenienced by forestry, the former needs to nest by big lochs, the latter needs solitude. Thirty-nine per cent of the British population of dunlin breed here and they must have the labyrinth of small pools to find the aquatic insects essential for raising their young. Hen harriers are intimidated by the closeness of forestry. They are not woodland birds.

This forestry has brought in birds otherwise common elsewhere. The chaffinch (*Fringilla coelebs*) and coal tit (*Parus ater*) join other birds in the forest canopy. Hooded crows (*Corvus corone*) nest in the tops of conifers and feed on dunlin chicks. It is thought that forestry increases the number of other predators such as foxes, providing them with cover, and they feed on the chicks of hen harrier and other rare breeding birds. Short-eared owls (*Asio flammeus*) nest in the Flows and their populations are often controlled by the abundance of short-tailed voles (*Microtus agrestis*). Voles increase in numbers during the first few years of a plantation, thus increasing the population of owls, then between ten and fifteen years voles decline, followed by owls.

An onerous effect of forestry is on the land, for it increases erosion of peat and soil. Drainage ditches release acid from the surrounding soil and this in its turn releases aluminium into the water. Aluminium is toxic to fish and fish are an important resource for tourists. Over 10,000 people come to fish in Caithness and Sutherland each year. Another formidable threat is to the spawning grounds of fish, many of which are centred upon only a handful of streams. Forestry draws off water from the streams bringing them down to dangerously low levels. Shallow water is dangerous to the spawn as it can die in cool temperatures.

The problems from forestry seem to be unending. Fences stop the red deer from moving from their traditional wintering grounds to the higher grounds of summer, but what of conservation. The foresters reckon to leave some larger pools for wildlife, but they plant to the water's edge. They remove all important smaller pools. In fact, they admit that forestry is no place for moorland birds. If the advice of the NCC is to be upheld then a perfect solution would be to safeguard 60 per cent of the Flow Country by leaving the most important peat and blanket bog areas, leaving the best habitats of the greenshank and dunlin, the river catchment areas of the black-throated diver and the areas which support the merlin and other rare breeding birds.

In late January 1988 Malcolm Rifkind, Secretary of State for Scotland, announced in the House of Commons that a new 430,000a (172,000ha) SSSI had been designated in the Flow Country. However, he has allowed further afforestation on some sensitive areas which the NCC believe should be left unplanted whilst a two year moratorium takes place.

The suite of birds most likely to be found in forestry plantations are essentially 'nut-crackers' (my terminology), those birds whose bills enable them to tackle cones and remove the seeds. However, there are few of them. Gregarious crossbills (*Loxia curvirostra*) are an obvious example. When feeding young they can regurgitate 100 seeds at a time, straight from their collecting trips. There are also redpols (*Carduelis flammea*) and siskins (*Carduelis spinus*) which tease seeds from cones, even those of the non-conifer, alder (*Alnus glutinosa*). Siskins have actually benefited from the spread of conifers to increase their overall population.

In northern England, Wales and Scotland there are a few birds of prey which are associated with forestry stands, but they are not representative of the mass of forestry in England. They include the goshawk (*Accipiter gentilis*) and sparrowhawk (*Accipiter nisus*). In southern England the hobby (*Falco subbuteo*) and honey buzzard (*Pernis apivorus*) are rare visitors and nest-builders in pines, the honey buzzard requiring tracts of adjacent open ground for hunting.

*Common bird's-
foot-trefoil*

There are a few inadvertent success stories for insects in forestry plantations. Two butterflies have prospered well, even expanded their ranges. These are the orange tip (*Anthocharis cardamines*) and the wood white (*Leptidea sinapis*). Both species have benefited from the long rides that are found in forestry plantations. The rides represent linear nature reserves, akin to motorway verges, though they are still open to man-the-picker-trampler-and-collector.

Wild flowers prosper too. Fortunately for these two butterflies mentioned above, the everlasting pea (*Lathyrus*) and bird's-foot-trefoil (*Lotus corniculatus*) keep the caterpillars of the wood white going, and, in the ditches, the lady's smock (or cuckoo flower) (*Cardamine pratensis*) keeps populations of orange tip up. Notice that the Latin name of the orange tip's food plant is reflected in the butterfly's name.

Another virtue of the forestry ride (for butterflies that is) is the edge-effect. Each edge of a ride, makes a significant habitat, somewhat shaded, certainly extensive. It is often the nature of rides that the original flora tries desperately hard to assert itself in this little haven devoid of the strict regimented regime of the forestry stands.

The Forestry Commission are actually trying hard to make forestry areas better for wildlife. They are now providing many more compartments in the wood for plants and animals and their rides will not always be the monotonous hard-edged rides we are presently used to. There will be different patterns of thinning, for instance chevron-thinning (describing the pattern) or herring-bone thinning. Their ideas are to allow much more light into the rides (i.e. making them wider) to stimulate plants. They have to balance maximum yield with minimum cost. The width of the ride is critical. The length of shadow cast by a 33ft (10m) tall tree at noon on the equinox is used as a guide! The more sun let in, the better for wildlife.

Above Healthy saplings were left in the traditional management of hedgerows so that standard trees would result *below*.

◆ WOODLAND CONSERVATION ◆

The three leaders in woodland conservation in Britain are the Woodland Trust (WT), the National Trust (NT) and the Royal Society for Nature Conservation (RSNC).

The NT claims that its conservation movement acquires a new woodland reserve on average every 12 days, a rate which it has sustained for 25 years (that was up to 1988). It has 680 woodland reserves.

The WT claims to acquire a new woodland every fortnight. Its startling rise to the cause of woodland conservation has been dazzling. In ten years it leapt from 1–50,000 members and sometimes its gains members at the rate of 100 a week. Its appeal is that it has one dedicated aim, to conserve Britain's native woodland for future generations. A modest subscription goes towards buying woods, often threatened, and saving them from the hands of developers. The public are free to walk in their woods which are found throughout Britain. The WT have promoted various tree-planting schemes such as the enormously successful 'Plant a Tree in 1973' and 'Plant one More in 1974'.

The RSNC own many hundreds of woodland nature reserves through their network of County Trust for Nature Conservation. You are strongly advised to become a member of your local wildlife trust and find out about your local woodland reserves. There are forty-seven country trusts nationwide and they offer plenty of opportunities for actively participating in woodland conservation, for adults and children alike.

A neighbourhood watch scheme for over-looking the welfare of trees is sorely needed in every town and village in Britain, particularly on building sites. There are some basic facts of 'life' about the well-being of old trees that developers ought to know about.

Developers in urban sprawl areas often specifically leave mature trees on site so that when the houses or factories are built the trees will be an amenity. In other words they want to keep the tree. However, by breaking all the 'ground' rules they end up killing the trees they really wanted. So it is incumbent upon us all to politely inform developers on site about the code (this has to be handled with great tact!).

◆ WOODLAND AND TREE SURVEYS ◆

Woodland surveys are very important and should be carried out in all parishes nationwide. The Council for the Protection of Rural England (CPRE) have been encouraging people to make woodland and tree surveys in Britain since 1972 and offer a free leaflets on *Making a Tree Survey*. The point of a survey is to see what sort of woods and trees are present, with a view to highlighting those habitats and individual trees that require conservation.

Above Herbiciding of field margins still continues in places. *Below* Farmers have to accommodate EEC policies and change land use accordingly.

◆ TREE PRESERVATION ORDERS ◆

One measure that we all have at our disposition as ordinary members of the public is the Tree Preservation Orders (TPO). Now this may sound as though it is designed only for individual trees, but it is also there for the protection of groups of trees or woodland. The only proviso is that the trees in question must be of amenity value.

If, during the course of doing a survey you find some fine examples of trees, notify your local planning office or tourism and recreation department, with all the information including a rough map and simply ask if they could be considered for TPOs. The legislation is there for everyone to avail themselves. It is designed to protect trees, and habitats with trees, such as hedgerows which all of course contain trees, for future generations. It was enacted in the Town and Country Planning Act of 1947 and given more 'bite' in the Town and Country Amenities Act of 1974.

Should you find a developer destroying trees that you feel should be conserved under a TPO then ring the local council offices immediately and ask for a TPO to be put on the particular trees. The TPO can then be immediately effective.

Anyone who lops, tops, or fells a tree with a TPO on it is liable to a fine of £1,000 or twice the value of the tree, whichever is the greater, upon conviction, or an unlimited fine upon indictment. There is a problem for the council highways department, who look after many of our TPO trees, especially in conservation areas, as technically, permission has to be granted from the Secretary of State, to trim trees, say of overhanging or storm-damaged limbs, even when this is in the best interests of public safety and of the tree.

◆ SMALL WOODLANDS ◆

Great possibilities exist in all parishes for the conservation of small woodlands. They can be both productive woodlands, perhaps as coppices, and at the same time be of educational and amenity value to the community. The wildlife of particular woods might be already very rich, but you can improve the quality of the wood by some simple procedures. If dark and gloomy in the wood, open it in places as glades and let the sunshine in. This will encourage wild flowers to bloom the following spring, and this, in turn will encourage insects, which will encourage birds. Dig a pond and you will find this colonised almost overnight with amphibians, water beetles and it will become a breeding site for dragonflies and damselflies. Leave as much fallen timber as can be left safely for the public.

Create a nature trail through the wood, making sure that the route passes as many different habitats as possible. Make a short nature trail (say under a mile) for those less mobile. Make a longer one for schoolchildren. Build a hide in an area away from a footpath. Perhaps there is an active badger sett to keep records on, or a fox's earth? Make bird boxes and bat boxes and have these set high up in the trees; north face of trees for bats, south side for birds. The possibilities are endless.

The great importance of small woodlands is the part they play in the continuity of the countryside. If small woodlands are connected to other woodlands by hedgerows and copses there is direct interplay of species which can move around from one wood to another. This does not restrict their breeding. If species are isolated within small woods they are obliged to breed amongst themselves. This then throws up genetic defects and the performance of populations diminishes. Let's hope that extensification and set-aside measures set the reinstatement of hedges which will help to link up much of the British countryside.

HEDGEROWS

⋅ WHAT IS A HEDGE? ⋅

Hedges are many things to many men, but they are all man-made or man-managed habitats. They are not natural habitats (with few exceptions), although they may look and feel like a well-balanced habitat. They may be made of upstanding slate, a turf (peat) bank, a living thicket or artificial dead hedge. The definition begs another question, what is the function of hedges, for if they are man-made they must have been made for some reason?

The reason has been to keep stock in, and to keep other stock out of a certain parcel of land. A type of prickly barricade, stockade or corrall to control animals. The most effective prickly deterrent I have ever seen is a re-constructed Indian corral used by southern Californian Indians

A well laid hedgerow with chestnut posts driven in as supports, sapling trees woven in between the posts and hazel woven along the top of the hedge.

chestnut post

made of a living wall of prickly pear (*Opuntia sp.*). The European equivalent of the 'thorns', in comparison, is much more tame.

When the primaeval forest was cleared, man enclosed and protected his hard-earned acres from the ravages of wild animals and stopped his valuable domestic animals from escaping into the forest. In some cases he would have used the natural forest edge as a barrier, and much later, these would have become a permanent part of the countryside patchwork. These are 'shaws', which actually have a slightly different meaning today, but they were hedgerow barriers, that we now regard as being of great longevity.

In the Weald of southern England at least, the sticky clay had to be drained for any useful agriculture to start, and a drain or ditch would have been dug alongside a hedgerow. Both the hedgerow and the open ditch may well have been made at the same time. If not, the hedge provided a suitable place to run the drain along. Today, many of our farm hedgerows have adjacent ditches, which, incidentally boost the wildlife potential of the hedge with this extra complement of wild flowers.

So primarily the function of a hedge is as a barrier. However, it has other very useful functions for farm management. During hot summers, animals like sheep gather in the cool of the hedgerow. It is undisputed that sheep actually do rather well on lowlands and uplands without much, if any shade, but when shade is available, they will use it.

sapling tree   hazel

Unseen functions of hedgerows that we have learnt a great deal about over the last 40 years of unadulterated land abuse, is that when *in situ* they protect the land. Take them out in horrendous numbers, as we found out in East Anglia, and the dry soil blows away. The fertility and fabric of the soil gone in a puff of wind, only to assuage modern agricultural methods and feed food mountains.

The mere presence of a hedgerow is of vital importance to hundreds of animals, it is a 'natural fuel station' for birds, mammals and insects and is a linear refuge or corridor for wildlife. Much of this is discussed later in greater detail.

◆ HOW LONG IS A HEDGE? ◆

This question appears on first sight to be a little obtuse. How long is a piece of string? Actually there is some sense in the apparent arbitrary length of hedges. Scholarly work done by Messrs Pollard, Hooper and Moore has shown that many hedges are multiples of one chain. This old unit of length was equal to 22yd (20m). These workers found that 10 per cent of all the numerous hedges they analysed, were actually of 10 chains (200m), or one furlong. Furlong comes from 'one furrow' or the length commonly ploughed with a horse and plough. The next greatest incidence of hedgerow length were those of 8 chains (160m) or 12 chains (240m). The shortest lengths of hedges these workers could determine on Ordnance Survey maps (1:25,000) was 2 chains or (40m).

It is interesting that the means of ploughing has left its mark on hedges we see today. If a team of eight oxen were used these needed a great deal of room to turn round at the ends of the rows, so a slight curvature of the hedge was a great advantage. See if you can spot any of these curved hedgerows.

One of the most notable hedges in seventeenth century England was that belonging to John Evelyn at his Sayes Court estate at Deptford (south-east London). He was a keen gardener, writer on gardening matters and a keen sylviculturalist (one who specialises in trees and shrubs) and personally planted out his 400ft (122m) holly hedge. It eventually grew to an impressive 9ft (2m 75cm) high and 5ft (1m 52cm) wide. Whilst away on business Evelyn rented out his estate to the Czar of Muscovy (Peter the Great), who severely damaged the house and grounds including the hedge. Part of the Czar's eccentricity was being wheelbarrowed through the hedge for kicks! Naturally Evelyn took action and asked Sir Christopher Wren to assess the damage, which was billed at over £400. Nothing remains of Evelyn's glorious hedge, but today the tallest is the one at Meikleour in Perthshire which is about 80ft (24m) high and 570yd (0.6km) long.

Why not measure some of your own hedgerows in your parish. Pace them out and see if you can find any which are multiples of one chain.

Trying to work out the hidden history of a hedge is one of those golden ecological opportunities that everyone has on their own door-step. A hedge of say, 400 years old, crossing a field may have had as many as twenty-four owners (twelve each side with 30 years for each generation). Land did not change hands that quickly long ago, but the example helps to illustrate the point that each hedge we try to interpret has had many different management regimes imposed upon it. Some farmers cut holes for gates, selectively take out tree species, plant favoured ones, cut back the edges or abandon the hedgerow for decades. Combined with the natural death of trees and storm damage our specimen hedge may look a bit threadbare and worn in places. It is stimulating, though, to put back the clock and try to interpret the management strategies which have produced what is before our eyes. It's essential to know the whereabouts of your ancient hedgerows before you start to conserve them.

◆ HOW OLD IS A HEDGE? ◆

Considerable debate has centred on the age of hedges and learned professors have, within the last five years, crossed swords on their interpretation of the evidence available. Some maintain that most of the hedges we see, at least those that were *in situ* up to 1950, are comparatively recent at about 200 years old. Other authorities have found recent evidence that shows that some parts of the British countryside show vestiges of Iron Age antiquity. They believe large numbers of hedges in most counties except Huntingdonshire, are actually pre-1700. The myth, then, that most hedges were planted in the last 200 years is well and truly cast aside.

The oldest documented hedge in Britain was at Bamburgh in Northumberland in A.D. 547. Mention is made in an Anglo-Saxon chronicle that Ida of Northumberland had to erect a hedge around his new settlement. What sort it was we do not know. Saxon hedges may have been 'dead' hedges, barricades of hawthorn or blackthorn set up to protect man and beast. At least we have the record from the King of Wessex (688–694) that hedges were used to limit cattle grazing. The progression from dead hedge to 'live' hedge would have been quite rapid. Those prickly customers, hawthorn and blackthorn (otherwise called quick and sloe respectively) were 'quick' to grow when struck in the ground. Perhaps their usefulness was realised unintentionally.

None of these ancient hedges survive, but traces of the ancient 'shaws' of the original forest, left as hedgerow stands, are thought by some to have survived today. If you want to try and find some, you will have to work very hard and conduct a serious hedgerow survey of your parish.

A thorny hedge was always a useful barrier to have at the top of a defensive earthworks, such as those at Offa's Dyke (east Wales), the

Giant's Hedge (Cornwall) or Fleam Dyke (Cambridgeshire). Today some parts of Offa's Dyke are visited by 100,000 people and the 168mi (270km) long Offa's Dyke path, some of which is continuous with the Offa's Dyke, is regarded as Britain's most vulnerable ancient monument. The earthworks were made in the eighth century to keep the Welsh out of Mercia.

The very nature of England's green and pleasant land with its patchwork countryside is created by hedgerows and fields. It is mostly a man-managed landscape that has been continually added to (and taken away from) by man. When he lived in the woods, dens and hursts he began to cut the forest, open up new glades and divide the land. The boom in division of the land and the partitioning of parcels of land to the common man occurred with the enclosures acts. Unbelievably there were 2000 of them passed between 1603 and 1903, most in the reign of George III. Other authorities go back even further and see two great enclosure movements. The first between 1460 and 1600 took place particularly in the Midlands and Northumberland, and the second occurred between 1740 and 1830. In both periods commons and wastelands were divided up for sheep grazing. Lowland England up to about 1,000ft (300m) was mostly set out in its patchwork of small fields and hedgerows by about 1815 and this is when most of the roadside hedgerows were established.

> The little lanes of England
> That wind amongst the trees
> They spread a net of memory
> Across the seven seas.
> They move the exiles heart
> To thoughts of home again.
> The little lanes of England
> Have magic in their train
> *Anonymous*

◆ Ageing a hedge

There is a simple and reliable method for dating a hedge. First, choose a hedge and, at a randomly chosen point, pace out 30yd (27m). Second, count the number of different woody plant species found along that length. Third, repeat the process two or more times and finally, make an average of your records. If, for example, you found five woody species in the first hedge section, six in the second and seven in the third the average would be six.

You do not have to know the identity of each of the species. The important point is how many *different* species there are. Beware of woody suckers and climbers such as ivy and honeysuckle; these are not included in the calculations. Climbing briar roses are included. The method does not presuppose that you should be able to identify everything you see. The task is even more difficult in the winter without tell-tale leaves, but if you do experience difficulty take along a friend and a good tree identification guide for help.

The number of different woody species can then be used to calculate the age of the hedge fairly accurately. Brilliant ecological work carried out at Monks Wood Experimental Station (Cambridgeshire) on all sorts of hedgerow in their area, has shown quite positively that for each woody species found on average in a hedge we can allow 100 years, more or less. Thus a hedge with an average of six woody species, would be about 600 years old. If your study is done locally the results are more meaningful than if they are from several counties. If, as the researchers did, they compared the results from 227 hedges in Cambridgeshire, Devon, Huntingdonshire, Lincolnshire and Northamptonshire, there was an error of about 28 per cent, so that for a 1,100-year-old hedge the variation on age estimation was plus or minus 200 years. This is because there are more variable factors, such as soil types, aspect and different regional species to consider than in one area, such as your own parish.

From this work at Monks Wood, it follows that it takes about 100 years to get a new species fully integrated into a hedgerow, sufficient for it to turn up, on average, in the sampling methods. It is preferable to do as many 30yd (27m) samples as possible to calculate a more accurate figure. This neat theory takes into consideration the fact that the hedge was man-made in the first place and had, presumably, one species planted throughout its length. The interesting ecological point is how does a new species get itself integrated along a hedgerow? Dispersal of seeds by wind and mammals gets seeds to many habitats, hedges as well as fields, and it is the survival of specimens in this hedgerow and their capabilities to conquer the constraints of competing species, which allows them to prosper, albeit over 100 years.

Your sampling work will give you a measure of this ecological competitiveness in action, as you will have recorded more woody species present than are recorded in the average number. Perhaps 11 species in total but six on average. There will be one or two woody species not represented anywhere else; surely newcomers which are getting themselves integrated in the habitat. This can be verified by looking along the hedgerow. Can you spot the newcomers, or those departing?

Try this method out along your parish boundaries and the boundaries of old estates for these are likely to yield some of the most interesting, if not some of the oldest, parish hedges. You will have some surprises in trying to trace their origins and routes. If your parish has an old estate or deer park, it is worth searching local documentary records as there are often written accounts of hedges giving details of when and with what species they were planted.

◆ HEDGE HABITATS ◆

What a superb habitat a hedge is! It has all the appearances of an excitingly rich habitat full of wild flowers and animals. As it is mostly an artificial, man-made habitat, this speaks volumes for the natural powers of colonisation.

The hedge habitat can be thought of as two separate parts (see below). Cut in section across the hedge there is the main body of the hedge and, on either side, a triangular addition. These seasonal additions add to the overall potential of the hedge habitat and considerably to its surface area. In the case of roadside verges they may or may not be cut, but when present they offer a very useful area for colonisation by plants and animals. Many perennial orchids have strong colonies here. On the agricultural side (it may be on both sides) there are greater chances that this extra area will be cut right back to the bare minimum and ploughing will be right up to the edge of the hedge. However, some farmers are being encouraged financially to leave a strip of land round their fields, adjacent to their hedge for the protection of wildlife. Some of that wildlife is beneficial, rather than detrimental, as some farmers feared.

As spring progresses, such plants as cow parsley, hogweed and lady's smock grow taller providing cover for ground nesting birds. Pheasants

Section through a hedgerow to show spring and summer extensions to habitat.

roadside extension

road

take advantage of the added cover.

The word 'hedgerow', as distinct from 'hedge' gives another dimension to the hedge habitat and introduces the concept of *linear nature reserves*. Like canals, rivers, railways, roads and motorways, the hedgerow system can be a continuous, meandering habitat criss-crossing the countryside. In 1973 the Council for the Protection of Rural England (CPRE) calculated that there were 600,000mi (966,000km) of hedge. At an average width of 2yd (1.8m) this represented the equivalent of a nature reserve (if compressed into one area) of 440,000a (176,000ha). At the time this represented about twice the area occupied by National Nature Reserves in Britain – quite a formidable habitat wrapped up in hedges.

There was a time when a large mammal, such as a fox, could have walked across country, fictitiously, from Land's End to John O'Groats without breaking cover from a hedgerow, such was the continuity. On a more local scale the importance of hedgerows as *corridors* for movement of small and large mammals was invaluable. As hedgerows were taken out, so the animals which had to cross open ground, were seen and shot. If they did not want to cross the ground, they became isolated in limited hedgerows and woods. One community of animals living in a wood, would be cut off from another wood because the hedgerow link had

main body of hedge

fieldside extension

field

gone. For plants and their seed dispersal along the hedge, the same fragmentation and limits to their powers of dispersal were also evident. Such a concept of the isolation of woodlands and the animals within them, is called the 'woods as islands' effect and it is precipitated by hedgerow removal.

◆ HEDGEROW FLORA ◆

The hedgerow habitat is such a lively place for wild flowers, set off with warm banks, wet ditches, shady corners and thickets ideal for a rich suite of plants. In fact over 250 species have been recorded from hedgerows.

Banks of primroses are a springtime delight, complete in their two floral forms, the pin-eyed and the thrum-eyed (get down and have a look at the different arrangement of the female parts, the gynaecium or pistil of old, sticking up like a pin in one, and half way down in another). Have you seen the primrose-coloured brimstone butterfly, a winter hibernator, pollinating primroses? It is a rare sight, never forgotten. No damp ditch would be complete without the cuckoo flower, or milk maids (*Cardamine pratensis*) which shows off its white and pink flowers for the female orange tip butterfly (*Anthocharis cardamines*) to lay its eggs on. It will also lay on the Jack-by-the-hedge (*Alliaria petiolata*) which keeps growing bigger-leaved and taller as the summer progresses.

If you are fortunate to be in a sunken lane, note the polypody fern (*Polypodium* sp.) often seen around the base of the standard tree, or the hard fern (*Asplenium* sp.), so hardy that its green fronds survive all winter.

No hedgerow verge is ever without cow parsley (*Anthriscus sylvestris*) or its umbelliferous friend, hogweed (*Heracleum sphondylium*), or occasionally the alien from Italy, the giant hogweed (*H. mantegazzianum*), even the purple-speckled hemlock (*Conium maculatum*) which could, to inexperienced eyes, be confused for angelica (*Angelica sylvestris*). Tall hedgerow members in the shade below overhanging branches lurk foxglove (*Digitalis purpurea*) and mullein (*Verbascum* sp.) both biennials, and the tall codlins and cream (named after apples with cream), also called the great willowherb (*Epilobium hirsutum*).

It is interesting how many medicinal plants occur along hedgerows. Wet ditches used to support plenty of the meadowsweet (*Filipendula ulmaria*) with plumes of creamy flowers at the end of its tall stems. It is important pharmaceutically for its active ingredients. Drainage and the general cleaning up of the hedgerow verges has seen the decline of this species. Of ancient importance are the woundworts (*Stachys spp.*) species, of which hedge woundwort (*S. sylvatica*) was supposedly used for staunching the flow of blood. Fleabane (*Pulicaria dysenterica*) is such an attractive plant which draws insects, especially butterflies, but when dried and ground into a powder, it is a deterrent to insects in the house.

The stitchworts (*Stellaria* species) of which the herbalist Culpeper spoke in the seventeenth century, are common hedgerow plants but one doubts whether they were actually employed for sufferers of the stitch! Burdock (*Arctium lappa*), whose huge leaves are some of the biggest along the hedgerow has been used with dandelion (*Taraxacum officinale*) as a refreshing drink. Mugwort (*Artemesia vulgaris*) and that common wayside plant coltsfoot (*Tussilago farfara*) have also been used for this purpose. Do not confuse the wayside winter heliotrope (*Petasites fragrans*), an introduced species with an over-powering fragrance, for coltsfoot, even though its leaves look more like a coltsfoot, than coltsfoot.

There are two widely distributed orchids of old hedgerow banks and roadside verges. These are, in order of emergence, the early purple orchid (*Orchis mascula*) and the common spotted (*Dactylorhiza fuchsii*). Established colonies of these orchids can be very numerous, several hundred together. A few country wildlife trusts actually have roadside nature reserves designated where there are interesting collections of plants. The local authorities are informed not to cut the verge during the inappropriate months. Most trusts do not have such contingencies, so there is much scope for this sort of hedgerow verge protection.

One of the most attractive places to find plants is on a hedgerow bank. Sunken lanes are even better, as the overhanging vegetation provides a humid environment in which ferns can grow as well. The sunken lanes were formed in the pre-tarmac period when soil and lane material was simply washed downhill during storms, leaving the hedges high and dry on the hedgerow bank, in some cases, now, 20ft (6m) above the lane. It is in the ensuring tangle of vegetation that wild flowers prosper.

The cuckoo pint (*Arum maculatum*) is always a familiar sight on the hedgerow bank, present for most of the year. It pokes up its new spathes (the leaf-like cowl which surrounds the flowerhead) at the New Year and in the autumn showing off its poisonous red berries borne high on its long spadix (the rod-like part of the flower). Earlier in the spring the spadix heats up and attracts tiny insects which it imprisons for a day or so, simply for pollination to take place. The insects are then released none the worse. Surprisingly, this was a useful plant in the last century. The roots were dug up and sent to a factory in Weymouth to make 'Weymouth sago' and starch for gentlemen's collars. Today it is no longer used. Digging up any plant is illegal anyway, unless you are the owner or have the owner's permission.

Hedgerows can become tangled up with all sorts of climbers such as honeysuckle, which Shakespeare called the 'woodbine' since it binds up otherwise healthy trees and saplings. Foresters still do not like it, but it is good for wildlife. Its fragrant blossoms attract plenty of insects. Wild hops (*Humulus lupulus*), native to Britain, are also perennial, and die back completely to the hedgerow base each year. Continental hops have been introduced to England as well: 'Hops, Reformation, bays and bear, Came to England all in one year' and many have escaped in hedgerows in Kent, East Sussex and Worcestershire.

The lyricists Flanders and Swann had words to describe (or to remember) the correct way in which some hedgerow climbers fought their way to the top. Their celebrated song 'Miss-alliance' graphically describe the marriage between the honeysuckle and bindweed, all tendrils and stems round each other... 'Said the right-handed honeysuckle to the left-handed bindweed, Let's get married'. To the accompaniment of the piano the first verse of the long ballad went:

> The fragrant honeysuckle spirals clockwise to the sun,
> And many other creepers do the same.
> But some climb anti-clockwise
> The Bindweed does for one
> Or Convolvulus to give its proper name.

The hazel dormouse (*Muscaradina avellanarius*) lives in thick hedgerows where it makes its nests by using the fibrous thread it strips from honeysuckle. Summer nests are made higher up in the hedge (I have found them 3ft (0.9m) up in a privet hedge) or above grass tussocks, whilst hibernation quarters are in more secure areas low down in hedges or within thick grass tussocks.

Another common hedgerow climbers is the white bryony (*Bryonia dioica*), usually called red bryony since it has clusters of red fruits. It is a member of the climbing cucumber family and has always been regarded as a medicinal plant. It is also the 'mandrake' which is said to emit blood-curdling screams if you ever try to pull up. Its roots can be formidably large and were collected, dried and ground up to make powders suitable for aiding conception. Black bryony (*Tamus communis*) on the other hand is another native which also has red berries but has shiny ovate leaves. It is, surprisingly, a member of the yam family.

Most noticeable on a frosty winter's day is the wild clematis (*Clematis vitalba*) otherwise known as traveller's-joy and old man's beard. It ranges wildly through the hedgerow, but grows best on chalk. At the edge of a yew wood it will smother trees, sprawl over the canopy and have jungle-like lianes inside. Only after a hard frost do the fluffy clematis fruit heads look really white, like an old man's beard.

Ivy is a perfect menace in the hedgerow, often forming complete sections by itself at the expense of the smothered plants it uses for support. It is part of nature's mopping up system, helping to clear out unsuccessful saplings and taking over old trees, strangling them to death. It is always a pity to see apparently healthy trees succumb to ivy, but you can help to redress the balance, by cutting through ivy stems. Some of the more vigorous trees do, however, manage to shrug off ivy. Ivy has its advantages in the well-being of the hedge and that is through its contribution as a feeding-station for insects.

◆ HEDGEROW TREES AND FRUITS ◆

Long ago the sign of a good woodman would have been the tidy rows of standard trees along the hedgerow. Every few yards any promising sapling tree would have been left to become a fine standard tree, suitable, in future generations, for felling to make timber-framed buildings. It required generations of woodmen to nurture and cajole trees through to maturity, carefully trimming the sides to give the longest run of unknotted wood possible; the best wood was always oak.

Fine oaks in hedgerows often look majestic, especially if they are allowed to develop their proper tree profile. Along road hedges they often have their lower limbs cut off to allow traffic movement. This definitely detracts from their aesthetic appeal. Some of these trees may become 'stag-horned' (see page 26).

The wildlife associated with oak, detailed in the previous chapter, is an important factor in the overall wildlife appeal of a hedgerow, for the greater number of insects, the more birds move in to feast on the insects. Walking along an oak hedgerow you would not fail to notice the hard brown oak apples. Each of these is caused by a small wasp-like insect which bores into the stem and causes this plant reaction. Galls like these were once used to make ink, for they are rich in tannin pigment. There are other insect-induced galls on the tree, including the currant galls hanging on the catkins and the spangle galls as small discs smothering the undersides of the leaves. Oaks are not alone in having galls. Most trees have their own and they are usually host-specific. Perhaps the obvious one in the hedgerow is the witch's broom – nests of small branches on silver birch (*Betula pendula*) caused, in this case, by a fungus. Look out for the fluffy balls of the Robin's pincushion, another gall, this time specific to rose and caused by an insect. They used to be collected as a 'bedeguar' and hung round the neck to ward off whooping-cough.

Where hedgerows show a legacy of former layering (see pages 58–9), some of the neglected shoots of the laid hedge can become quite large and dominant. Hornbeam (*Carpinus betulus*), with its smooth bark is often seen growing up from a mass of contorted branches formerly laid professionally.

The holly, or holy, tree (*Ilex aquifolium*) is a regular member of hedgerows and is often left well alone by people who have a religious respect for it. If it was cut more frequently the extra growth at stock level would add to the not inconsiderable amount of prickly leaves low down. The berries are useful as a source of food for birds. Hollies which are left to grow up in a hedgerow can become large standard trees often with accompanying saplings.

Fruit productivity is at its best in a hedge with hawthorn, nothing else is quite so extravagant. The haws droop from the trees in autumn when the pigeons are too fat after harvest; it really takes a cold snap in the New

Year for them to be exploited to the full. The efficiency with which hawthorn harnesses sunlight and converts it into millions of tons of fruit, most of it eventually to be lost to fungi, birds and mammals, has baffled scientists trying desperately to harness the sun's energy.

There are actually two species of hawthorn, separated by their different shaped leaves and fruits. The common hawthorn in England is *Crataegus monogyna*, much planted in hedgerows. It usually has one stone in each ovary, or, later the haw. The Midland hawthorn (*Crataegus oxyacanthoides*) is much less common and has two stones in each haw. Traditionally, the miners in the Midlands used to chew the leaves of their hawthorns on surfacing from the mines, to refresh the taste in their mouths. There are delicate hues of pink and white blossom seen in hawthorn, even attractive doubles. In normal years the showers of blossom in late May really look as though snow has fallen over the hedgerow. The bees are everywhere, for nectar runs fast and furious in a hot May. The hawthorn marks the end of the spring flowers, and the beginning of the fortnight 'June gap' when very few plants are in flower, in anticipation of the summer flowers such as clover which come out from mid June onwards. If there is a cold snap in the June gap, bees can starve to death. Hawthorn's other name of May blossom is usually appropriate, but when the season is running late, the May can come out in June.

Although hawthorns are the predominate plant species found in English hedgerows, it is not the only useful species with vicious prickles. The sloe or blackthorn (*Prunus spinosa*) provides a myriad of sharp spines, captivated in its Latin name and an equally spiny relation is the bullace. This is not so common, but where it occurs the fruits can be super-numerous, especially in an overgrown hedgerow. They are dull and dirty orange when ripe but are wonderful stewed up, quite unlike the sloe which is half the size, blue with a delicate bloom of wild yeasts brushing the surface.

The great fruit producers of the hedgerow are hawthorn and blackthorn, which are good for birds. Many other hedgerow fruits attract human visitors out for a good walk blackberrying in the autumn. The black morsels are not evolved for us, they are designed to be eaten by our feathered friends who kindly dispose of the seeds en route somewhere else and aid in dispersal. The hips and haws are red to attract birds, yet the hips are loaded with vitamins A and C. Efficacious rose hip syrup is still sold in the high street today. In the last war, rose hips were collected for the war effort – as were foxglove fruits loaded with their digitalin drug ready for extraction. No hedgerow would be complete without foxgloves up under the shade of the hedge, their splendid biennial flowers reaching maturity in the second summer – their prolific seeds being knocked out of the fruit pods by fox cubs tumbling down the bank.

The rabbit-proof bark of the elderberry (*Sambucus nigra*) allows it to

Above Straw burning is dangerous to habitats and wildlife. *Below* The interface between farming and heathland is vividly shown here with both improved (green) and unimproved (brown) land.

prosper in hedgerows. There are noxious chemicals in the bark that rabbits do not like and they leave well alone. The fragrant sprays of elderflower are eagerly sought by wine-makers, as well as insects such as hover-flies which enjoy the nectar. The purple-hued fruits fall quickly if not eaten by birds like blackbirds and thrushes or collected by wine-makers.

Some hedgerows have not looked the same since the 1970s when the elms were at their best. Sadly we are 12 million elm trees the poorer. The elm suckers still struggle on in hedges littered with the sawn-off trunks of their parents. One day a clone of elms, naturally resistant to the fatal fungus will arise and elms will return to their former glory. In the meantime, we see less of the wych elm (*Ulmus glabra*), our only native elm, and the English and smooth-leaved elms (*U. procera* and *U. minor*). The last two formed hybrids which, before the 1970s crash, successfully colonised hedgerows by suckering. The slow movement of elms along our hedgerows by suckering has been traced from East Anglia into southern England via hedgerows. There were severe outbreaks of the disease in the 1930s and again in the 1960s and 1970s. The organism which caused the death of the trees was a fungus which was carried from tree to tree by tiny elm bark beetles which accidentally collects the fungal spores on its body.

◆ HEDGEROW LOSSES AND GAINS ◆

The awful statistics of hedgerow loss are not going to be drawn out here in full repetitious detail, however tragic a loss for our rural landscape. Instead, results of recent research carried out by the Department of the Environment (DOE) and the Countryside Commission (CC) sheds some light on new activities. The good news is that we are planting hedges rapidly, and the bad news is that we are still ripping out hedgerows at a faster rate than before. So what is new?

The declining league table for hedgerows still extant in England and Wales is as follows:

1947 there were 495,000mi (796,950km) of hedgerow
1969   ,,   ,,   437,000mi (703,520km) of hedgerow
1980   ,,   ,,   406,000mi (653,660km) of hedgerow
1985   ,,   ,,   386,000mi (617,600km) of hedgerow

During the period 1980 to 1985, 23,500mi (37,600km) of hedgerow were removed, but 2,500mi (4,025km) were planted, making a net loss of 21,000mi (33,810km) for this period. The alarming point is that the rate of hedgerow removal has leapt from an average of 2,600mi (4,186km) per year in 1947 to 4,000mi (6,440km) a year in the 1980s and the greatest loss has been in East Anglia and the East Midlands. This attrition of Britain's countryside fabric never seems to get better. Lest

Above Migrating wildfowl are attracted to reservoirs and find sanctuary in some. *Below* This flap allows the badger to continue its nocturnal wanderings without admitting rabbits.

you should get a pessimistic attitude towards hedgerow loss, take heart in the financial inducement for farmers not to farm and the work of conservation bodies in promoting hedgerow conservation on farms.

◆ CONSERVATION OF HEDGEROWS ◆

Peter Brandon's prophecy in *The Sussex Landscape*, 1974 was that in the 1990s most of the shaws, hedgerows and copses of the Weald will have completely disappeared, except in the marshiest of places, is already true, in places. The sweeping away of the hedgerows in the rolling countryside of England began in earnest in the 1970s from Land's End to the cliffs of Dover. North and South Downs were considerably opened up by some unscrupulous farmers, one of whom paid a fine and served a prison sentence. Most farmers, however, respect the country-side and will do their best for wildlife, without putting themselves out of business. They all have to adapt readily to ever changing market pressures.

Many cases demonstrate the absurd nature of 'subsidies for destruction', a theme brilliantly pursued by pioneer ecologist Marion Shoard in her erudite book *The Theft of the Countryside* (this *must* be everyone's introduction to problems of the countryside). It also highlighted the ambivalent position of the government, on the one hand (as Ministry of Agriculture, Fisheries and Food, MAFF) offering cash incentives to destroy hedges to make fields bigger, and, on the other (via the Nature Conservancy Council, NCC), by taking farmers to court for wantonly destroying known biologically important sites (SSSIs), formerly registered by the NCC.

'Improvement' of the land must be put in farming and ecological context. From the farming point of view, land which is unproductive, for instance uplands, moors, bogs, woods and hedges which get in the way of bigger, more productive farms, used to be eligible for financial subsidies. Hedges could be removed and a cash subsidy given for their destruction. The theory being, that the country would be the richer for the extra mount of food that could be grown on the recently cleared land. From the ecological point of view, such subsidies represented a depletion of the natural habitats for wildlife. Hedges acting as refuges for wildlife and a loss of the very fabric of the countryside which we call Britain. The loss of hedges is hardly improvement to conservationists. The overproduction of food for the Common Market, at the expense of such hedge habitats has made Britain, much the poorer. To what end?

One of the threats to flora and fauna by isolation has already been mentioned. You cannot take away thousands of miles of hedgerow habitat and not lose anything. Plants have lost all the hedgerow margins, headlands and shaws as possible places for exploitation. Many plants are under threat of extinction and have been since the Botanical Society

Spindle tree

Hedge bedstraw

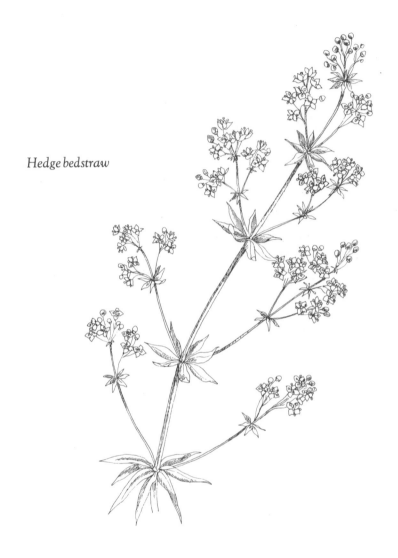

of the British Isles published their list of 30 threatened species in 1970. The table on page 69 includes some surprising entries. First, crab apples, which some may know from gardens, but its real habitat is the hedgerow where its decline is ominous. The more that disappear the less there are to replace them. It is the same with many hedgerow trees. There is a greater proportion of older trees than younger ones coming along to replace them. Work out the proportion for your own parish. Second, the chequer tree, which gives its name to those pubs called 'The Chequers' after its bark which has a light and dark colour. How many Chequer pubs do you know which have chequer trees next to them? Plant one now! They are not being replaced as they disappear from our hedgerows. Their autumn tints are fabulous and rival any field maple (*Acer campestre*), which is actually more at home in a hedge than a field.

VULNERABLE WILD PLANTS OF
·THE HEDGEROW·

Taken from 'The Botanical Importance of Our Hedgerows', in *Flora of a Changing Britain* (1970) published by the Botanical Society of the British Isles. It reads 'I think the following 30 species (excluding *Rosa* and *Rhus*) may become extinct in some areas in the next 30 years largely as a result of hedgerow removal.'

Common name	Latin name
Moschatel	*Adoxa moschatellina*
Fragrant agrimony	*Agrimonia procera*
Bur chervil	*Anthriscus caucalis*
Hairy brome	*Bromus ramosus*
White bryony	*Bryonia dioica*
Rough Chervil	*Chaerophyllum temulentum*
Traveller's joy	*Clematis vitalba*
Small teasel	*Dipsacus pilosus*
Spindle	*Euonymus europaeus*
Hedge bedstraw	*Galium mollugo*
Lady's bedstraw	*Galium verum*
Hop	*Humulus lupulus*
Honeysuckle	*Lonicera periclymenum*
Crab apple	*Malus sylvestris*
Corn parsley	*Petroselinum segetum*
Wood meadow-grass	*Poa nemoralis*
Wild pear	*Pyrus communis*
Buckthorn	*Rhamnus catharticus*
Sweet briar	*Rosa rubiginosa aggregate*
Wild madder	*Rubia peregrina*
Stone parsley	*Sison amomum*
Goldenrod	*Solidago virgaurea*
Wild service tree	*Sorbus torminalis*
Dogwood	*Swida sanguinea*
Black bryony	*Tamus communis*
Upright hedge-parsley	*Torilis japonica*
Wayfaring tree	*Viburnum lantana*
Greater periwinkle	*Vinca major*
Lesser periwinkle	*Vinca minor*
Sweet violet	*Viola odorata*

Sweet violet

Crab apple tree

The moschatel is a delightful shady hedge-bank species, limited to fewer and fewer stations. You can come across it on chalk on the North or South Downs and its delicate square flower heads are so reminiscent of a Town Hall Clock that it is often called just that! The bedstraws as their name implies were used for stuffing beds and eiderdowns, and their frequency along waysides and in meadows used to be more common than today.

Take care of the plants in a hedgerow and the animals will invade by themselves. The insect hordes will arrive from across the Channel and North Sea, migrant butterflies, day-flying moths, ladybirds, maybugs, aphids and hoverflies swarm into Britain each year as immigrants. Not just in hedgerows but everywhere. No passport control for them – even for the banned Colorado Beetle, an unwanted American alien resident on the continent!

Surprising as it may seem, it is thought that no animal species in England has become extinct through hedgerow removal. Millions of animals have been put out though, by loss of their favourite habitat. Large mammals like foxes and badgers have been considerably inconvenienced and small mammals have had to pull back their ranges into woodland refuges. It speaks highly of animals, and insects in particular, that they have not reached the ultimate state of extinction through hedgerow removal, since they have such good powers of coping with habitat change. Insects are small, fast breeders, capable of finding new niches in life.

Where hedgerows provide a warm south, or south-west facing aspect, they provide hot spots for insects. One entomological observer at the end of last century at Ilfracombe (Devon) recorded masses of butterflies on ivy blossom on 9 October the ivy 'almost hidden from sight by a countless multitude of butterflies and moths'. They comprised red admirals (*Vanessa atalanta*), painted ladies (*Cynthia cardui*) and a single Camberwell beauty (*Nymphalis antiopa*). Such a smothering of ivy can often be witnessed in gardens and along hedgerows, with honey-bees eager for the last nectar source of the year. At Ilfracombe these insects were immigrants, demonstrating that hedges also serve as fuelling stations for hungry insects.

Forty bird species depend on hedges for food, shelter and nesting. There are ways to increase the potential of your own hedges. Where there are good thickets of hedges and masses of fruits there will be birds enjoying the food and shelter. The richest sort of hedge is one close to woodland where you might expect nineteen species in a $12\frac{1}{2}$a (5ha) farmland site. This has been carefully worked out by ecologists from Monks Wood. The next most bird-rich site was a tall hedge with seventeen species, followed by a short hedge with a dozen species and an open arable hedge with a ditch which claimed seven and a half species. The worst site was an open arable hedge with ditch which could only run to five species.

Clearly, if you wish to manage a hedge for birds, instead of for profit you would allow the farm hedge to blossom to a recommended 6ft (1·8m) tall and just over 1yd (1m) in width.

The numerical density of hedgerows in your own area is important when it comes to nesting frequency. There are perhaps twenty birds' nests to be found in an average mile of hedgerow. In Devon, where there might be 30–35mi (48–56km) of hedgerows in a square mile, the loss of 1mi (1·6km) of hedgerow would not significantly alter the number of nesting birds. In East Anglia where there are many fewer hedges a loss of 1mi (1.6km) of hedgerow may be catastrophic for birdlife.

If you are establishing a hedge, go for beech, blackthorn, crab apple, hawthorn, gorse, hazel, holly, hornbeam, field maple, cherry plum and willow – these are the common species suitable for planting. Do not be tempted to go for ash, elder, holm oak, sycamore or whitebeam, some grow too thin and tall, others are invasive. No-one should ever touch sycamore since it is such a pervasive 'weed', and, it is an alien, a fifteenth-century import from eastern Europe. Regard sycamore, and wild rhododendrons as well, as ecological disaster zones! They cause conservation corps working parties hundreds of hours of hard toil pursuing their fecund offspring. Beware of box, broom, cherry laurel, cypress, laburnum, rhododendron and yew as they are poisonous to stock. Do check the right soil type required for each tree species. There are plenty of field guides and leaflets on tree planting.

Lest some people think that all farmers sow only seeds of gloom and doom in the environment by taking out hedges, let it be said that most farmers will try very hard to accommodate all conservation interests without putting their livelihood at risk. They have to change with the times, especially with constraints from the European Economic Community (EEC). They have been planting hedges on farms extensively in the last decade or so. A great deal of effort has gone into making farmers more ecologically aware. This has been masterminded by a regional group of FWAG representatives, representing the Farming and Wildlife Advisory Group. They liaise between ecologists and farmers and do a brilliant job.

Now there is even better news and it is all to do with the recent trend of paying the farmer not to farm – a seemingly ridiculous thing to do 20 years ago. Now we prefer to conserve the countryside rather than to make food mountains. Inducements of £300 per 2½a (1ha) are now made to farmers in East Anglia and the South Downs in Environmentally Sensitive Areas (ESAs) to lave a 20ft (6m) headland uncropped at the edge of their arable fields. Another inducement is to allow £100 per 2½a (1ha) for fields margins which are left completely free of chemical spraying during the year. These 'conservation headlands' are eagerly welcomed by conservationists since they allow birds, butterflies, grasshoppers and wild flowers to prosper. They are also welcomed by Game Conservancy. They will help to redress the sterile environments created

Wild service tree

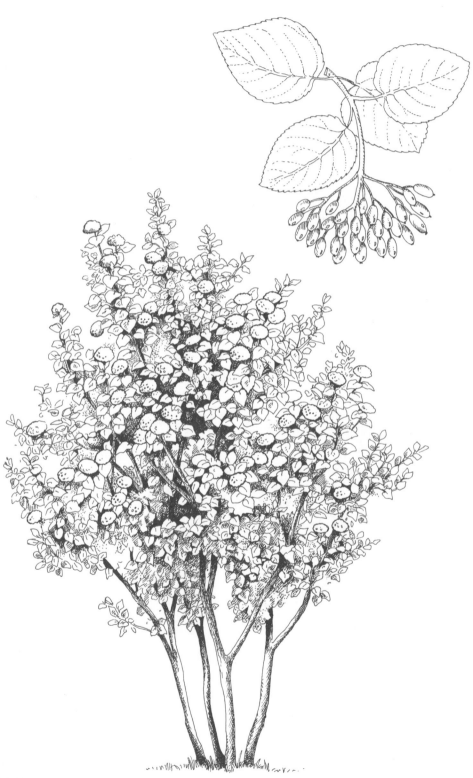

Wayfaring tree

around vast fields where blanket herbiciding caused so much destruction. We all welcome the return of wild hedgerows.

Hedges are essentially made up of trees, cut to make to a hedge. Thus, it seems right and proper that TPOs (see page 50) are available for hedges. Should you find the existence of an ancient hedgerow in your parish, perhaps through hedge-dating, then it might be deemed appropriate by your local authority to place a TPO on it. Notify the council in writing of the particular hedge, the interesting combination of species and the estimated age and the council will consider putting a TPO on it. It can be made effective on the day you apply and this can be an advantage should you feel a certain hedge is in peril of being destroyed by a private individual, farmer or developer. Anyone can apply for a TPO. Exploit your rights if necessary.

THE ORGANIC GARDEN & FARM

· WHAT IS ORGANIC? ·

The New Oxford Dictionary definition of organic is food produced without artificial fertilisers or pesticides. Before the 1940s when 'nasty' agrochemicals were invented, everyone gardened in a traditional fashion using manures as fertilisers, soapy water against insects and crop rotation. Inadvertently these methods were beneficial to the environment, took little from it and gave a lot back. The relatively harmless chemicals of the pre-1940s were 'inorganic' and included salts of potassium and sodium; however, some like sodium arsenate (containing arsenic) were potentially hazardous if you didn't wash your cabbages! Then came the 1940s and a new wave of chemicals hit the market, these were the 'organic' ones containing chlorine and phosphorous. Twenty years later the carnage of dead birds and mammals told the sorry tale of accumulation in animal food webs. Rachel Carson told the tale in *Silent Spring*. Few have heeded her advice today.

Ironically, the environmentally-destructive agrochemicals which are abhorred by organic farmers are, scientifically classified as 'organic' in comparison to inorganic ones – a very confusing misnomer. Strictly, 'organic' chemicals are complex molecules containing carbon and hydrogen combined with other elements; they leave dangerous residues in the soil and water. To a farmer who has 'gone organic' the term means growing plants without using dangerous organic chemicals. When an advertiser says 'contains organic ingredients' he does not mean organic in its chemical sense. He means the opposite, using 'natural' products like fibre, manure and trace elements. The term 'organic' has come to mean a more 'back to earth' approach to farming and gardening, relying on mulching and manuring (cultural control) and biological control.

Organic farmers like to work with nature, respecting the soil micro-organisms and the natural mineral cycle which exists there. They also employ nature to fight nature, as in biological control methods. They use naturally-occurring fungi and bacteria, specially-prepared, to kill pests, use plant chemicals as fertilizers and insecticides, produce their own manure and use a great deal of common sense in planting and working the soil. Organic farming is for 'thinkers' since they are (hopefully) always one step ahead of pests, parasites and pathogens (a micro-organisms which cause disease). 'Organic' also means a healthy respect of the wildlife of gardens which contain useful predators and beneficial insects.

A lot has been written about organic farming and gardening, about 'going organic', 'the organic way', the 'organic movement' and the eccentricity of organic farmers. Essentially there is nothing new in this continued revival of an age old system that brings good results. It is simply a pleasant realisation by an increasing number of people that tasty foods can be produced quite innocuously.

The frightening thing about organic chemicals is that they are unseen, lurk in the environment, pollute food webs and threaten our survival. It is claimed by some that the average person eats 11lb (5kg) of agrochemicals in their food each year!

• ADVANTAGES OF ORGANIC FARMING •

Organic farmers aspire to a chemical-free environment and wholesome foods without any of the hidden additives. Harmful waste products and residues left over from a series of chemical applications do not contaminate their soil. It is enhanced with fibres and compost which provides a better texture (the coveted crumbliness of the soil) for the next crop. The soil develops enhanced water retention qualities and improved fertility. 'Organic' soil becomes more 'sustainable' for future crops with roots, manure and fibre turned back into the ground. There is less likelihood of nutrient loss (leaching) from the organic soil and the foods produced are not tasteless, faceless wonders without bulges and blemishes.

Less produce may be produced by the organic method (about 10 per cent down) but the price obtained for chemical-free food makes it more worthwhile. There may be increased problems from weeds and insects but these can be overcome. More mechanisation and reversion to older methods and techniques may be necessary to sustain an organic approach but this is not altogether a bad thing.

◆ WHAT CAN YOU GROW? ◆

The organic farmer can grow just about everything and there are plenty of people now making a living from organic produce. This ranges from beef reared on flower-rich meadows providing all trace elements required, 'green-top' milk, organic wheat for making bread, organic soft and top fruit and vegetables galore including organic leeks and garlic. Try some organic yoghurt. There are organic wines from all over Europe, not forgetting organically-grown flowers. The *New Organic Food Guide* lists 600 organic outlets in Britain and Ireland, some near you. Safeway led the way in having organic foods in their supermarkets.

◆ THE ORGANIC CONSUMER ◆

What matters most is what the housewife wants, her requirements are simple: no additives, no pesticides, no artificial fertilizers, no growth promoters, just the *wholesome* product with no extraneous additions and no legacy left in the environment.

How can we be sure that the foods we buy are genuinely organic? There are watchdog groups which check up on food but it is difficult, for instance on the production of the twenty or so products from several countries which go into a product like muesli. Some organic produce in British shops comes from Holland where pig-slurry is used as a manure. It is reported that the pigs themselves are not necessarily fed on organic foods, so how far does the organic trail go back? Land previously treated with agrochemicals should be left fallow for three years. Organic produce in Britain now takes 15–20 per cent of the market (1987 figures).

◆ THE ORGANIC PRODUCER ◆

How do you combat the pernicious weeds and the hordes of insects which seek to strangle, starve and destroy your wonderful crops? What is permitted under the organic law and what is not?

◆ Chemical control

The 'chemical' stand of the organic farmer is not entirely clear-cut and provides critics of the organic systems with fuel. In principle all organic agrochemicals are banned from any organic farm since contamination of product and soils occurs. Inorganic salts, such as the traditional Bordeaux mixture containing copper sulphate and lime, are permitted. Sulphur is permitted in the manufacture of wine; ground rock minerals such as phosphate and potash and calcified seaweed are permitted by some. So far everything is very clear. However, the principles upon which cultural control of pests is based relies heavily upon the natural chemical nature of some plants. The system of growing aromatic plants next to your crops relies upon volatile odours (chemicals) deterring passing pests.

As organic farmers use nature to fight nature, it is only natural that they use the chemicals of chrysanthemums and derris plants to deter insect pests. The 'acceptable' pyrethrin powder or the derris dust which are extracted commercially from these two groups of plants have an acceptably low toxicity in the environment (i.e. they break down quickly) and are 'safe' to humans. Organic farmers do not permit man-made 'pyrethroids' such as Permethrin which are chemically very similar to pyrethrin. The reason is that it leaves residues in the ground for up to 12 days and is unacceptably poisonous to beneficial insects.

Man-made chemicals which mimic the sex scents of pest insects are permitted – these are called pheromone-lures (pheromones are insect hormones used as odours). They work on the principle that males are attracted to a volatile substance, a sex scent, emitted by the female. By synthesising the female scent it is then used to attract males so that they can be eliminated. A good example of this is against codling moth which is a real threat in orchards.

Inorganic soaps are permitted by organic farmers, some impregnated with nicotine as an insect deterrent. The soap allows the water to spread over the leaf surface as a wetting agent, which effectively drowns insects in the water film. It is useful against aphids on roses and vegetables.

◆ Cultural control

Cultural control is not perhaps the first method an organic farmer thinks of for eliminating pests. Cultural control involves the use of prudent gardening techniques and an understanding of the deterrent nature of some plants and, if well thought out, can be very effective indeed.

Weeds are combatted in a variety of ways. Thinking in the long term, weeds can be suppressed by mulching. This simply means covering the ground with a suitable material, black plastic, wood chippings, paper, cardboard, old carpets or underlay. The sooner this is done before planting the better and a year is not too long to kill off all deep rooted rogue weeds. Hoeing is tedious but most effective if done regularly. Weeds can easily get out of control but do not lose heart, as some have done in the organic movement, persevere with a different method – perhaps your crops are planted too far apart? Sow a 'green manure' (see page 82) to cover a vacant plot liable to become weedy after harvesting. Broadcast your seeds to give a thicker growth of plants less liable to fill up with weeds.

By growing onions next to carrots and runner beans, insects are deterred by the strong-smelling odours.

Insects have highly sophisticated ways of finding their host plants, zooming in on colour, scent, identifying the outline of their food plants and flying close to the ground. A little knowledge goes a long way. Erect a fine netting barrier around the carrots, since most carrot root flies fly at ground level. Alternate rows of crops (inter-planting) so that, for instance, the cabbage root fly cannot recognise the outline of the cabbage against the ground.

Another method to deter insects, is to grow plants which give off strong deterrent odours alongside your crops. Onions and garlic are good with carrots and beans or, lay tomato leaves near the cabbages. These are all excellent companion plants.

◆ Biological control

Organic farmers encourage all wildlife of the garden which destroys pests. Not only are the beneficial animals used like hedgehogs and bats or ground beetles and ladybirds, but there is an array of living organisms, many of them minute, to fight pests. They range from tiny mail-order mini-wasps (*Encarsia formosa*) which parasitise greenhouse aphids or a South American mite called *Phytoseilus persimilis* to kill its cousins the red spider mites in greenhouses, to a bacteria (Bactospeine) or virus formulated to kill cabbage caterpillars.

Ladybirds are valuable beneficial insects. Here, seen devouring aphids.

◆ Composts and manures

Organic farmers are very proud of their home produced compost and a great deal of energy is expended in getting it right. It is worth visiting the Henry Doubleday Research Association trials near Coventry to see the different methods in action, shredding, mixing with urine, covering or making liquid compost are all demonstrated.

You can grow your own compost in the form of 'green manure'. These are plants which are either grown to be turned into the soil or harvested for the benefit of the soil especially when there is extra space in the garden in the autumn. The most mineral-rich plant you could grow is comfrey (there are several species) since this can be cropped at ground level three times a year and fermented into liquid manure or turned on the compost heap. Other plants which can be used are mustard, winter tares (vetches) and beans. There are several other species which can be grown for this purpose including: buckwheat, an attractive North American plant which brightens any herbaceous bed and adds calcium; clovers, rye and lupins which are all rich in phosphates.

A natural fertilizer much used by organic farmers is liquid seaweed ('Seagold Calcified Seaweed') rich in trace elements ideal for soft fruit, e.g. gooseberries, and lawn improvement. If you want you can have barrels of special earthworms working on your behalf making some of the best natural compost available, simply by throwing them clippings, cuttings and old leaves as food.

Organic farmers and conservationists already dabble in the use of earthworms for compost-making. There are even earthworm farms which supply the demand for backyard compost-making courtesy of earthworms. It is a very sensible thing to do since earthworms are one of the major beneficial animals in the garden and they may as well be harnessed into action.

There are twenty-five species of earthworm in Britain and one of them, the brandling worm (*Eisenia fetida*) much prefers warm, rotting vegetation for breeding. There are actually about six earthworm species which may be found in your compost heap. All earthworms eat rotting vegetation and this helps the decay process releasing nitrogen and other minerals to the soil.

In the wild or in the garden earthworms serve an excellent role in recycling old leaves and other vegetable matter. Under ordinary pasture the concentration of earthworms may be three million per acre, probably representing more than the weight of livestock grazing the ground above. They drag leaves down into the ground, break them up, digest them and allow useful bacteria to work on them.

Charles Darwin, the first person to write a comprehensive book on the ecology of earthworms (*The Formation of Vegetable Mould through the Action of Worms*) worked out that earthworms bring about 18 tons of soil to the surface of an acre of pasture each year. This mixing of the soil is ideal for making the soil crumbly, a highly regarded feature and essential for root growth and survival. Darwin was an admirer of eighteenth-century parson-naturalist, Gilbert White of Selborne, Hampshire, who did not regard earthworms very keenly 'gardeners and and farmers express their detestation of worms'. Today earthworms are riding high on a wave of fashion.

◆ THE FUTURE ◆

Many more farmers are now getting together and regulating organic produce. The Organic Farmers and Growers (OF & G) have led in this direction and have a considerable membership. The guidelines for organic foods were originally set by the International Federation of Organic Agricultural Movements (IFOAM) and OF & G are pressing for legally enforced standards today.

Regular meetings are under way between interested groups and government to issue useful guidelines, definitions, labelling criteria and a special logo for 'registered' organic growers and to strike some sort of unity between the organic societies and groups. The organic movement has never had government recognition or backing but now seeks to amend that and encourage EEC support.

Pasqueflower

FARMING ARABLE & FRUIT

Only a minority of farmers cause horrendous damage to the countryside and visibly scar it. It is easy to assume that all farmers are like this, but they are not. It is a question of balance. It is possible to encourage farmers to leave wilder corners, headlands and hedgerows. With the new phase of extensive farming – the opposite of intensive farming – farmers are recommended alternative ways of boosting their income without pursuing intensive measures. With set-aside, field margins may literally be set aside for the benefit of flowers and wildlife.

We must understand that the quaint British countryside that we all love is a patchwork of artificial habitats, completely altered by man from the original vegetation and habitats once present. The fact that wildlife is richly represented in the woods and hedgerows is proof that flora and fauna can withstand such a complete upheaval and habitat change. We must all seek to conserve wildlife, whilst exploiting the riches of the land; two apparently conflicting aims.

• FWAG •

The amicable union between farmers and conservationists is tactfully arranged by a network of people throughout the country called FWAG-men, or FWAG-persons. These are members of a group called the Farming and Wildlife Advisory Groups (FWAGs) set up in 1969 by a number of interested parties including the National Farmer's Union (NFU), the Ministry of Fisheries & Food (MAFF) and the Royal Society for the Protection of Birds (RSPB), under whose wing the organisation is run. In 1987 there were forty full-time Farm Conservation Advisers in almost every county of England and in some parts of Scotland and Wales. It is promoted and supported by the Farming and Wildlife Trust, a charity set up in 1984.

Their aim is to complement farming and wildlife, so that benefits can accrue on each side. They fill a useful advisory gap left by the Wildlife & Countryside Act of 1981 which did not spell out the implications for the ordinary farmer. The majority of farmers have land which is not scheduled as SSSIs (see page 141) and no clear cut guidelines. They liaise with the Forestry Commission on such projects as the Broad-leaved Grant Scheme or with the Game Conservancy on their Cereal and Game Birds Project. They recommend to farmers alternative methods of generating income by diversification, for instance coppicing woods, or digging ponds for fish farming. If this is not enough there are demonstration farms, where farmers can see, first hand, how a new project works, and there are always lists of farmers only too willing to let naturalists around their show-piece farms. You do not have to be a farmer to learn something from these farms. Small ideas can be adapted to suit your own backyard needs.

One of FWAG's shining examples of how they can manage a farm on conservation lines, is the 564a (225ha) estate at Brinsbury in West Sussex. With the help of a bevy of local naturalists, a complete ecological survey revealed over 400 species of flowering plant, seventy species of breeding bird and almost sixty species of mosses and liverworts. There were ancient woods and old hedgerows to protect. As always, it is only armed with an ecological survey of a site that you can start to conserve it. Historically, it was shown from old maps that ninety-six named fields had decreased to thirty-four in the last 140 years, thanks to hedgerow removal. Woodlands had increased from 46–68a. (18.4–27.2ha), though regrettably 36 per cent were coniferous.

As a practical-suggestion group, FWAG bridges that gulf between farmers and conservationists. There is still much antagonism within both factions. A few farmers still like to have a go at conservationists and take a distinct dislike to them – 'eco-nuts' to boot. Anti-conservationists can be quite verbose at times, often from a point of ignorance. To be fair, there are conservationists who cannot say a good word about farmers. Destroying any countryside is a cardinal sin whoever you are.

However, there is a middle road to take as a conservationist. A certain tolerance of the excesses of farming, industrialisation and urbanisation can result in plans being modified, new routes being negotiated, anti-pollution methods implemented, and some wildlife can be saved. It is always best to present the ecological argument to the farmer or developer, since they may not be aware of pressures on certain aspects of wildlife. In many cases alterations and modifications may be accommodated on genial grounds. The other road of complete antagonism often results in severe loss of habitats and wildlife.

• FARMERS AND THEIR LAND •

Arable land makes up so much of our landscape. How it is managed, by the few, influences the look of the countryside for the millions of others. Farmers represent only 1 per cent of the UK's population (56.4 million in 1984). Yet 80 per cent of the British countryside is farmland. Times have changed, before the enclosure acts, 80 per cent of the population worked on the land.

With our Common Agricultural Policy (CAP) in rather a mess and the over-production of food at the expense of natural habitats, we often question the prices we have to pay for farm products. It is interesting just to reflect on the principles of CAP with respect to our own experiences. According to the Treaty of Rome, the principles of the CAP are to (i) increase farm productivity, (ii) to ensure a fair standard of living for everyone engaged in agriculture, (iii) to stabilise markets, and (iv) to maintain 'reasonable' consumer prices.

Field size is gradually getting larger and larger, not always in those areas which have the richest type. Some of the poor soil of the Downs have been opened up on precariously steep escarpments, all for a little more pecuniary return. The landscape is disappearing rapidly, and in some areas it looks more like the north French arable wastelands or the North American grainbelt. One hundred acre (40ha) fields are all too common today, 1,000a (400ha) fields a little rarer. The price we have paid for these large wastelands for growing food is the loss of our pretty hedgerows and patchwork countryside. It could be argued, perhaps, that farmers have a moral obligation to respect the countryside that belongs to us all.

• PRACTICAL CONSERVATION ON FARMS •

Farmers are busy trying to re-instate many former habitats on their farms as well as creating others. Hedgerows, shaws, spinneys and ponds are coming back to life, whilst unproductive woods are now being opened up to the public for woodland walks. One such one in Sussex, the Arlington Farm run by farmer John McCutchan, won national acclaim in 1984 for its conservation of wildlife. The bluebell wood is breathtaking.

Around arable fields, times have been hard for wildlife over the last few decades. Woods and hedgerows have been grubbed out to obtain the maximum from the soil and many wild flowers, insects and small mammals have lost a suitable habitat.

Pioneer work on promoting suitable habitat for birds has been preoccupation of the Game Conservancy for a number of years. They have experimented with leaving unsprayed headlands or margins around fields, and have hoped that farmers will follow their advice. In fact there are now cash incentives to farmers to leave a headland of unploughed, un-herbicided strip round fields, but only in Environmentally Sensitive Areas (ESAs), see page 138. It is in these headlands that insects and other invertebrates thrive and birds move in to feed on them.

As might be expected, the incidence of grey partridges and pheasants too, increases dramatically when these margins are left. The ideal width is 13ft (4m). In 'normal' countryside with hedges but no margins, there may be four pairs of partridges in each square half mile, but this increases to twelve pairs with margins. The increased cover and insect food both make significant contributions to the birds' well-being. Incidentally, the maximum number of partridges per square half mile appears to be about fifteen pairs, as determined in pre-war arable pastures with hedgerows. The maximum number of any plant or animal that any habitat can reasonably hold, is scientifically called 'the carrying capacity'.

Farmers normally apply herbicides, insecticides and fungicides to crops to keep weeds, insects and fungi at bay. By controlling farmer's usual methods of dealing with these groups of pests, weeds may not be eradicated but wildlife prospers. Wild oats and cleavers are the main menaces. Conservationists seek to promote broad-leaved weeds that farmers prefer to eliminate. Delicate negotiations with farmers encourage them not to spread insecticide in the spring since the first 6 weeks of life for game chicks is critical. Spraying insecticides in the autumn is acceptable though. Fungicides can be applied in both the spring and autumn.

Normally herbicides eliminate weeds such as knotgrass, fat hen, mayweeds, chickweed and annual meadow grass which support numerous insects. The insects in their turn are the main food of game chicks. Following partridges fitted with radio-collars, ecologists have been able to determine that the birds used headlands more than the more widely dispersed hedgerows and shelters on average farms. Thus the use of herbicides strikes at the food of insects and the use of insecticides at the food of the birds and the life support chain is then broken in two places. The headland method of management conserves these essential links in the ecology to the benefit of plants and animals. The decline of the grey partridge in Britain was entirely due to the lack of insects such as leaf-beetles (on knotgrass), sawflies and plant bugs.

Small mammals do very well in headlands. Mice, shrews and voles prosper in the long grass and form tunnels beneath fallen grasses and tussocks. Barn owls almost certainly benefit from these new regimes – a great asset for this bird whose future is not secure. Wood mice and bank voles are particularly well represented on headlands. Butterflies like the green-veined white and the orange tip both thrive in this new habitat in the spring and seek nectar and lay their eggs on wild crucifers like lady's smock which grows prolifically along damp headlands.

Now that the headland experiment has been under investigation for a few years some of the rarer plants of the countryside are beginning to return to the hedgerow margin (or are being spotted by more eagle-eyed, conservation-minded ecologists). Pheasant's eye, narrow-leaved hemp nettle, rough poppy and shepherd's needle have all been spotted by elated botanists.

◆ Erosion and pollution

Arable farming involves intensive use of the land. No sooner is one crop harvested but the ground has to be replenished with more nutrients. Phosphates and nitrates are spread by the ton. The new crop is sown and within days of the old crop coming off, the shoots of the new crop burst from the ground. The crop turn-round period is hastened, the deleterious effect on the land is heightened and pollution prevails. It is impossible these days to leave fields fallow or indulge in the delights of a traditional Norfolk 4-year rotation. It's economy of scale.

Now that some areas have been denuded of their hedgerows and shelterbelts, as seen on the Downs and Chilterns, the bare expanses of chalk downs are highly susceptible to erosion. Steep hillsides run with soil at the slightest downpour and valuable soil ends up in the valley. Gulleys a yard deep scar the countryside. Stable hillsides with natural grassland, woods or scrub have changed overnight into slippery quagmires. Even respectable high streets of some Downland towns are regularly threatened by incursions of eroded material and crops, of almost avalanche proportions.

High winter and spring rainfall, as in 1969, 1977, 1979, 1983 and 1985, combine to cause severe soil erosion. Loss of up to 47 tons (48t) of soil per 0.4a. (1ha) have been recorded, equivalent to about 3mm ($\frac{1}{8}$in) of lost topsoil. Growing winter wheat has increased dramatically from 1,951,220a (780,488ha) to 3,414,634a (1,365,853ha) from 1969 to 1983. Tilling the soil for winter wheat during the worst winter months is sometimes asking for trouble. Many would argue that binding the soil with organic mulches would be a much better proposition.

It is a grim sight that we all have to put up with, bare expanses of ecologically sterile countryside, devoid of refuges for wildlife, yet we still overproduce food. Average yields of corn from the land are about 6.8 tons per $\frac{1}{2}$ acre (7t per hectare) and there is a select group of farmers in Kent and Northern France who are loosely banded together as a '10-tonne' club. They try to achieve this maximum yield from the best of their land.

When the farmer applies fertilizers or any other organic chemical to the land, some of this material and its residues pass through the soil immediately and makes it way to the nearest ditch, or, passes through the ground into the subterranean aquifer. The lost nutrients take their time in moving through the environment. From the ditch, the chemicals pass into streams, then rivers and are finally dumped out at sea. A poisonous legacy of toxic material makes its way to the ocean from our cherished countryside. We treat the ocean as a dustbin, forgotten, out of sight, and not affecting anyone at this stage. This one-way export and dumping of nutrients is summed up with the word leaching. Perhaps 'out of sight, out of mind' for the moment, but wait for the disappointing surprises in store when we want to exploit the natural resources of the marine environment!

Meanwhile in the local ditches which accompany arable land, the water greens over in a delightful ecological green! Duckweed blooms on the water surface to such an extent it crowds out most other plants. The ditch or stream surface looks as smooth and as green as a billiard table. Trouble lurks below though. The expanse of green acts in a similar manner to the canopy of a good beech wood, when in the summer, the leaves create a complete barrier for the penetration of the sunlight. Life below the duckweed becomes very murky with grim prospects. In effect, those plants which are rooted in the mud at the bottom of the stream cannot photosynthesise, cannot produce the life supporting oxygen which bubbles from the submerged leaves, and the aquatic invertebrates cannot extract the vital dissolved oxygen from the water because there isn't any.

This 'eutrophication', to apply its grand sounding scientific name, spells the end of small water beetles, water fleas, caddis fly larvae and dragonfly larvae which need to breathe under water. However, there is a life-line. When the deteriorating autumn weather arrives it pushes away this green canopy and the oxygen-poor environment can revert gradually to an oxygen-rich one. The reason why duckweed grows so well is simply because the water that drains from the surrounding agricultural land has so many agrochemicals in it, it is rather like a primeval soup, rich in nutrients. Plants of course love these conditions for active growth. It is on the same principle that nitrates and phosphates are sprayed on to grassland to improve the vigour of the crops.

◆ Nitrates and phosphates

Land cannot sustain production of crops year after year without returning some of the nutrients to it. The natural way was to leave the field fallow, often seeding clover, which is a leguminous plant with tiny root nodules containing nitrogen. Inside the nodules beneficial bacteria convert nitrogen into nitrites. These are then changed to nitrates. The clover crop would have been ploughed back into the soil to enrich the soil. Some of the nitrogen tied up in the soil is actually released back to the air by other bacteria. There is always about 80 per cent of nitrogen in air.

This cycling of nitrogen in nature is not the same for phosphates.

There is a one way movement of phosphates from the soil via the waterways to the seabed. Some phosphate is taken up by fish. Unless fish are caught and processed as fishmeal the phosphates never come back to the land.

Today's farmers have to empty the contents of those bright blue bags of artificial fertilizer on to their land each year in order to continue their business. To the farmers' financial loss, up to 90 per cent of the nitrates dispersed on the land may be lost into the soil almost immediately. The arable crops may not be growing actively and will not take up the nutrients, and, if wet, the nitrates will drain through the soil, either into a ditch or into a subterranean aquifer. Unlike phosphates or potassium, nitrates are very soluble in water and drain away quickly. Farmers continue with this extensive use of chemicals, since they still find that even the 10 per cent of the chemical taken up by the plants does make all the difference between profit and loss. The farmer gains, the environment loses.

The levels of nitrates in British waterways have been rising steadily since 1945. They have doubled in the last 20 years. The worst areas are the arable expanses of east and central England. The Department of the Environment published figures which showed that more of our rivers are classified as in a 'poor' or 'bad' state. Polluted waterways have risen from 2,128mi (3,426km) in the 1982/3 to 2,521mi (4,058km) in 1986/7.

There is another considerable loss to wildlife and conservation with this leaching of man-made nutrients through the soil. For man, there is the frightening possibility that much of the nitrates locked up in the subterranean aquifers will be discharged into our watershed areas that we rely on for our tap-water. Some people believe that up to 50–60 per cent of nitrogen in tap-water comes from agrochemicals.

There is evidence which suggests that once applied, nitrates may take 25–30 years to go through the system of soil, rocks and natural aquifers deep in the earth's crusts. There are a few alarming cases of fatal complications with babies whose drinking water has a high nitrate content. This very rare complication is called blue baby disease (or methaemoglobinaemia). It is not a public health hazard and the last recorded death was in 1950. There were 14 cases between 1950–1972.

Far more worrying is the loss of slurry from livestock units. A quarter of all farm pollution incidents recorded by the Water Authorities Association in a recent survey were found to have been due to slurry spills. A short spill from a farm with 200 cows is equivalent to untreated sewage from 3,000 people being discharged downstream.

The World Health Organisation (WHO) give recommendations about the safe levels of nitrates in tap water. It is 44.5mg per litre. The Department of Health and Social Security (DHSS) used to be satisfied with a level of 100mg per litre but after pressure have now revised these limits to 50mg per litre. The government propose special denitrification plants to rid tap water of its nitrates – an expensive operation. They also propose 'water protection zones' where nitrate levels will have to be regulated. In flat areas like East Anglia with large water catchment areas, the job of controlling nitrate percolation will be colossal.

River and stream water is almost certainly highly contaminated with nitrates and other chemicals if it flows through arable/agricultural land. There have been mishaps with wildlife dying from excessive nitrate levels in waterways due to leaching of agrochemicals from surrounding land, animal slurries, human sewage and cow slurries. Extensive drainage plans can cause a rush of nasty chemicals to surge down a river with catastrophic results. The sight of heaps of rotting fish and mussels is not a pretty one, and not a good advertisement for a healthy society, or for agriculture.

Organic farmers who use animal manure turned into the soil as their source of nitrogen, know that the nitrogen bound in with all the fibre will be released slowly but surely into the soil, without causing any harm.

If pollution of nitrates directly into the soil is not enough, there are other places that nitrogen gets to, before hitting the ground. Nitrogen from car exhausts and power stations contributes to acid rain, that scourge of recent years in Europe. Rain combines with the nitrous oxide to form a dilute nitric acid which falls on vegetation, killing it and turning lakes into fishless wonders. The major acid in acid rain is sulphuric acid, a combination of sulphur dioxide and rain-water. This spells acid death to plants, animals and habitats alike. Lichens are particularly pollution intolerant and cannot stand acid on their delicate surfaces. Smoky city centres are not for them.

◆ Straw-burning

Burning stubble after harvest was an innocuous activity. Today, sadly, stubble-burning has gone with the wind and been replaced with straw-burning. This is dangerous to habitats and wildlife. For too long now, we enter the autumn period with palls of smoke over our productive agricultural areas, e.g. Wiltshire, the Midlands, or Kent, as if in an aftermath of some war. People write to *The Times* to complain, but this is progress. Where else can farmers get rid of their straw?

Farmers no longer have the need for straw. Its old use as a bedding material for indoor livestock has waned as more and more animals are kept on concrete floors. To bale, move and store it would be a waste of money and no-one really wants it in quantity. So the farmer has no option but to burn it.

Ploughing it in is not effective. It does not degrade quickly. Burning experiments have shown that a 'good' burn returns far more nutrients to the soil than a 'bad' burn. 'Good in this sense is when the straw is very dry and most of it will eventually be burnt. Burning of partially damp straw does not give much back to the soil. However, on very large estates there has been a return to ploughing in straw simply to allow a quicker turn-round period between crops. Decomposition of the straw is aided by first cutting it up then ploughing it in with, guess what, nitrogen.

There is a perfectly adequate code of conduct of straw-burning produced by the NFU and MAFF in response to the general outrage about straw-burning. All contingencies have been anticipated in the code to stop flames leaping into hedgerows, woodland, nature reserves, and prevent problems caused by smoke.

It is a recommendation of the NFU that if any of the items in the code are broken a fine of £2,000 should be introduced for each item. To date only a handful of farmers have been reported and their fines have ranged from £15–20 to £250. The code is not legally binding but should be used in conjunction with the local bye-laws which seek to enforce them. In some parts of London and other urban areas, the bye-laws do not uphold the code. To put straw-burning in perspective, it is thought by some (in agriculture) to be less important than other rural problems such as sheep-worrying.

If you have any reason to complain about straw-burning, for instance hedges alight or any of the codes broken, then contact the police since they are duty bound to uphold the bye-laws. It is incumbent upon local people to police their own locality.

• ARABLE WILDLIFE •

Modern arable land can appear to be a void of nothing, of featureless land disappearing over the horizon, but it may well support a sizeable group of partridges scurrying away from you, or a flock of birds en route somewhere. Badgers, birds, insects and wild flowers hopefully crowd the headlands and hedgerows and provide some refuge for wildlife in this apparently alien environment.

Badgers may be an inconvenience to arable farmers in several ways, first, the construction of their accommodation. Most badgers live communally in a series of tunnels dug into a hillside. Sometimes this 'sett' area has been used on and off for several hundred years. Where possible, badgers do like to have dry accommodation and will tunnel underneath exposed layers of rock or sandstone. However, in order to maintain a healthy current of air through their sett (badgers are rather smelly, to us) they often construct a breather hole in the field above the sett. This is just kept open for the air to circulate, rather than being used by badgers. Its inconvenience to the farmer is that the wheel of a tractor may go down the hole, or worse, a valuable milking cow may break a leg in it.

Second, families of badgers have been known to feed at the edge of field of sweet corn, bending down the ripe heads and eating the fruits.

This is quite an innocuous occupation and tolerated by most farmers. Wherever there is a good mix of woodlands and pasture the badger has prospered. There are usually plenty of badgers where there is an abundance of dairying. Pastures kept grazed are ideal for badgers.

The badger likes to go out at night in search of food, especially earthworms. Where the milk herd has nibbled down the grass, the earthworms are exposed on the surface of the grass and are therefore easier for the badger to find. Thus the intimate association of the badger and the cow is forged. Criss-crossing through the legs of the cows as they feed at night, the badger offers the third, most frightening danger to farmers. The tuberculosis virus may be transmitted from badger to cow and thus from milk to man.

The fragile link, it is supposed, starts with an infective badger. Badgers have the habit of urinating intermittently whilst feeding so an infective badger passes its urine widely over grass contaminating it with the virus. The cow then ingests the grass plus virus and becomes infected. Great uproar occurred when the MAFF started to gas badgers to check the movement of tuberculosis (TB). Now a campaign of testing badger road casualties for TB has highlighted regions most affected with tubercular badgers. Areas found to be positive have the badgers gassed. It is in the interests of badgers to be killed if found with the disease, since they only suffer with it and pass it on to other badgers.

Otters used to run along much of lowland Britain following the water courses which twist and turn through the countryside. Now, unfortunately, their numbers have declined in areas where intensive arable farming has taken place. So much value is put on the land that river-banks and stream-banks are cleaned up, cut of their alder, willow and bramble thickets, and sheep often put down to graze right to the water's edge. Such an intensive environment is too much for the otters to cope with. It interferes with their way of life. They like to run along a good length of water each day to find their prey of fish and occasional small birds, whilst enjoying the safety of thickets and undergrowth; no thickets, no otters. Their demise from south-east England in the late 1970s was a typical result of the intensive agriculture.

Otters, are very much part of the healthier countryside to the north and west, unimproved by agriculture. Their presence, like that of butterflies, is viewed rather like an ecological indicator of a healthy environment and everyone laments their parting. Considerable effort was made to set up artificial otter havens, an on-going process, with much help from FWAG. In East Anglia Philip Wayre, the founder of the Otter Trust at Bungay (Suffolk), has designated over 186mi (300km) of waterway for otters. However, there is no legal force to look after these otter havens and only about a quarter of those designated by the Otter Trust are partially protected. The Otter Haven Project is also active in other parts of the country.

If loss of habitat is not enough there is another threat to otters.

Probably over 100 otters a year are killed accidentally in Britain in fyke nets (bag nets) and lobster creels (baskets). The otters become interested in the prey caught in the nets and creels, then become entangled and subsequently drown.

Whilst we still have the lowland stream or river in our minds we must also give a thought to the status of the mute swan on our British waterways. It has had to survive in this polluted environment lacking cover, and sadly, has come under attack from vandals with crossbows. Country swans actually fare worse than their counterparts in town. The reason is described as the 'bread factor' since town swans attract lots of attention from people and do very well on bread offerings. Country swans have to make do with what they can find along the rivers and streams. The results are for all to see: healthy pairs of swans with all their successfully fledged chicks surviving into winter, the country swans with just one or two surviving fledglings.

Harvest time is a problem for the rare Montague harrier in Britain, for it has recently developed the phenomenon of nesting in arable fields. After its demise in the 1950s and 1960s due to agrochemicals, its numbers have steadily built up, and in 1985 seven breeding pairs were recorded. It customarily breeds in arable fields on the continent but this was the first time that it had departed from its normal breeding sites, in conifers, heathland, moorland and in reed and sedge beds. Close liaison is necessary between conservationists and farmers to ensure that the chicks are safeguarded at harvest time, either left with a block of uncut corn around them, or gradually moved to the edge of the field in uncut corn. Either way, they have to be protected from their main enemy, the fox.

The Montague harrier's close relative the marsh harrier also breeds in lowland Britain but chooses small reed-beds adjacent to arable land. In 1985 their numbers had increased to thirty nests, from a single pair in the early 1970s.

It is lamentable that one of the key birds of cornfields has disappeared, the corncrake. It used to liven up the summer sound of hayfields with its call, mimicked by its Latin name. This bird may be a part of the English language but most of us have never seen it. When it was present in larger numbers it was more often heard than seen. We now have to go to Scotland or western Ireland where agriculture is not so intensive to see this shy little bird.

Geese are a major nuisance to arable farmers. Over the last few decades there have been fluctuating numbers of geese which graze farmland in coastal regions between Suffolk, Essex to Devon.

The main problem in the south of England is from Brent geese which winter in our warmer climates. They breed 3,000mi (4,830km) away the other side of Iceland and Greenland on Bathurst Island but cross the Atlantic to feed on European inter-tidal mud-flats. The Wexford Slobs in Eire is another of their favourite haunts. During cold winters the

The corncrake is rarely seen in cornfields these days.

birds are not content with feeding on eel grass and algae, but venture onto adjoining arable land. Here large flocks can cause significant damage within hours plucking out and eating winter wheat seedlings. Up to 50 per cent of an arable crop can be eaten this way. Wet soil can be puddled flat to cause caking later, disastrous for germination. Some say that it is only because we insist on growing winter crops that we have this problem. This is also the case with the severe erosion on the Sussex Downs.

Farmers have tried erecting scarecrows, vivid orange swivel boxes and broadcasting alarm calls but with limited success at deterring the birds. Farmers who can prove in court that the birds cause serious damage to crops are given shooting permits. This has occurred in East Anglia, Sussex and Hampshire.

Shooting permits are also issued annually to kill one of the world's most endangered species, the Barnacle goose on the Scottish island of Islay. It is a bird offered protection by the Wildlife & Countryside Act, yet the Scottish Office gives permits to farmers who can prove that the birds constitute a threat of serious damage to their crops. The birds breed on Greenland, 1,500mi (2,415km) away, and move to Scotland for the winter. The Greenland race of the goose, numbering some 23,500 individuals are part of the world population of 75,000. Thankfully there is now a RSPB reserve of 3,000a (1,200ha) on Islay which offers the Barnacles some sanctuary.

Space-saving modern fruit trees are grown like raspberry canes.

The old style 'top' fruit tree could produce good fruit for a hundred years or more.

Above The M40 passes through the Ashton Rowant National Nature Reserve and the vegetation has still not recovered.
Below Wildlife blossoms on motorway verges enriched with native and alien plants.

◆ FRUIT-FARMING AND WILDLIFE ◆

Fruit farming has intensified just like other forms of farming and the new orchard environment looks and feels different. The old 'top' fruit trees used to be good producers for a hundred years or more. Gypsies moved in to prune and cut back the trees which looked like dark monsters with arching limbs pointing to the ground. Now gypsies have gone, their huts have gone and many of these wildlife-rich man-made habitats have gone too. A technological departure has also been the tall ladders once used to pick the 'top' fruit from the highest branches. With modern 'top' fruit the word is redundant too.

So how rich was the orchard habitat that once was the common feature of the Garden of England in Kent or the Vale of Evesham in Hereford and Worcester? The long (un-herbicided) grass sprouted prolific fungi in the autumn such as the field mushrooms (*Agaricus campestris*), even the unpalatable yellow stainer mushroom (*Agaricus xanthoderma*). This was a good place to go for long walks, to exercise the dogs. There were interesting grasslands beneath the towering trees, full of butterflies like the meadow brown (*Maniola jurtina*) and the small heath (*Coenonympha pamphilus*). Occasionally the grass was mown. In the autumn when the air smelt of rotting fruit there were colourful displays of small tortoiseshells (*Aglais urticae*), peacocks (*Inachis io*), commas (*Polygonia c-album*) and red admirals (*Vanessa atalanta*) and squabbling wasps all vying for fallen fruit.

There were abundant supplies of mistletoe (*Viscum album*) for Christmas. Limbs sprouted with the orangey-green fruiting bodies of mosses which clothed the apple trunks and major limbs. Little owls (*Athene noctua*) were put up from tree to tree. Sometimes they rested or nested in hollow niches of the older trees. They liked this environment full of beetles and other small insects. Continental in origin the little owl has found Britain an ideal place in which to prosper.

There are still orchards like this in north Kent. However, the sad feature of this man-made environment is that there will be fewer and fewer of them in the future. As they come to the end of their life, or economic constraints dig deeper, farmers move to greater productivity off the same land.

One man-made environment is swapped for another. Modern fruit growers may cram in 500 fruit trees to the acre, growing them like raspberry canes. They have a life-expectancy measured in decades rather than centuries and are highly productive within 3 years. Ease of fruit collection and lateral branches bearing trusses of larger, more un-blemished fruit are added features.

Gone are many of the two thousand named varieties of dessert and kitchen apples, like May Queen and Orleans Renette (both dessert) or Peasgood's Nonsuch and Stirling Castle (kitchen). In their place are heavy fruiting varieties which are grown for their uniform appearance,

Above This canal in the West Midlands has become a wildlife haven with increased vegetation since it fell into disuse, note the changes between 1981 *above* and 1986 *below*.

not necessarily for their taste – did someone mention Golden Delicious? Demand from the EEC and retail traders requires standard fruit, often fairly undistinguished. Demand from the consumer should be the priority, a theme promoted by the British Apple Marketing Board.

Insects and birds have always featured strongly in orchards, though wood-boring beetles associated with old orchards are replaced with increased menaces from well established pests in the new environment.

Bullfinches (*Pyrrhula pyrrhula*) are a menace since they enjoy eating fruit buds. Living in small groups or flocks up to about 200, they descend upon orchards and can each eat up to thirty buds per minute. With their sharp-edged bill they can dehusk a pear bud in 6–8 seconds, a gooseberry bud in under 2 seconds. That is a lot of potential fruit lost. Bird scarers are designed to deter these hungry birds which prefer some varieties to others, for instance 'Discovery' apples or 'Conference' or 'William's' pears. In the garden they may not be so discerning as in a large orchard and they are also fairly partial to forsythia and daphne. The bird has had a price on its head since the Elizabethan period. A very pretty sight during the winter months with the bright scarlet colours of the male, the female has a more retiring suede-black colour.

Rabbits are frequently a nuisance in orchards and have to be excluded with continuous wire dug in all round. This of course excludes badgers (and foxes), which are pretty innocuous individuals in this environment. The nocturnal wandering of the badger can be respected by installing badger flaps. These are made of a hinged flap sufficiently large for the badger to pass through and made heavy with the addition of some lead strips. Placed in the line of an existing badger track or adjacent to a post for easy fixture, the weighed flap is just too heavy for a rabbit to push, but sufficient for a blundering badger to push its way through, very much undeterred by such a contraption.

Where deer are a threat to crops and gardens, stout deer fences (6ft 6in) (2m) high have to be installed. Lessons should be learned from deer netting first installed on Britain's motorways where a few unfortunate deer became impaled on the wire. There must be no rising ground adjacent to the netting to allow for a potential jump to be contemplated by the deer.

Honey-bees have naturally worked fruit blossom since recorded time, but their services are very much in demand today for their pollination duties. Each year thousands of bee hives are trucked into orchards just as the fruit blossom is opening. Their arrival is precisely timed since the bees need to visit the blossom just as it opens, rather than find an alternative local crop, which they might like better. All too often the bees head out of the orchard, straight to the nearest oilseed rape field. Two miles (3.2km) is the furthest that bees will venture in any direction.

If beekeepers gauge it correctly, the bees can be moved on to different crops as the season progresses, first on to almond blossom, then apple and pear, followed thereafter by oilseed rape in late May. Long gone is the traditional harvest of clover honey in July. August is for heather honey, if August is sunny.

From a conservation point of view honey-bees must be respected wherever they are working. The government seeks to uphold this principle and farmers have been taken to court over proved cases of bee poisoning. There are guidelines and codes of conduct. For instance if a field is going to be aerial sprayed there must be an on-site inspection to ascertain the proximity of housing, schools, recreational areas and of course beehives. Beekeepers can be notified of impending spraying and bees can then be kept hive-bound for a day whilst spraying takes place.

A typical case of honey-bee poisoning is a tragic affair with a characteristic pile of dead bees outside the hive. Poisoning in the field results in the bees limping back home, only to die inside the hive where their compatriots clean them out. The good thing from the chemical analysis point of view is that the bees can be sent off to a laboratory and checked for traces of the poison which killed them. Biochemists can determine the precise chemical from traces on/in the bee. Guilty farmers are then easy to trace via the NFU, MAFF or the old sacks and drums which litter untidy farmyards. Convictions have ensued from these most precise laboratory investigations. Farmers face stiffer penalties if they are proved to have been using a chemical which has been banned or is out of use.

The whole problem of honey-bee poisoning results from the conflicting interests. Honey-bees like the nectar which 'runs' when the flowers are open and it is sunny and warm. The farmer can only poison the insect pest directly (in the case of oil seed rape – the oil seed weevils) which lurk inside the open blossom when it is sunny and warm.

Honey-bees are as important today as ever for the yearly pollination of fruit trees.

LINEAR
RESERVES

One of the most interesting linear nature reserves is the hedgerow (see pages 52–75). Here the significance of three other linear reserves is discussed, motorways and roads, railways and canals. We have limited access to these but we are all observers as travellers, and see some things from the safety of the carriage, car or barge, that cannot be seen on the ground. We must all be aware of the flowering of the embankments and verges and the rich wildlife locked up in these linear nature reserves.

It is an increasing characteristic of Britain's wildlife that is squeezed further into the network of our own transport system. Driven out from the adjoining land which concentrates too much on industry, agriculture or urbanisation, wildlife has taken sanctuary in the last 'wild' habitats, albeit man-made grasslands and wastelands. All this has been unintentional, but it has been remarkable. A spectacle that everyone can see.

Observing from a distance is all that most of us can do for wildlife thriving along the motorway systems or along railways. Travelling in the cushy confines of the train or on a canal barge does have the advantage of witnessing playful scenes of foxes with cubs, that one might otherwise not see on foot. It is just as well that we are not allowed to trample over most of these refuges; if we were to, much of the flora and fauna would not be there.

• CHARACTERISTICS •

So what are the embracing characteristics of linear nature reserves? First, the reserve part. However we manage, or do not manage, the margin of roads, motorways, railways or canals, there will be always be habitat opportunities for different types of plants and animals. They find that life here is relatively unaffected by man's activities.

Lack of management is good for wildlife up to a certain point. Grassy areas may develop scrub and light woodland within 10 years, crowding out wild flowers and butterflies. Other species then start to take over at the expense of those that we might prefer.

Our preference highlights our own particular criteria for nature conservation (i.e. we like orchids or butterflies etc.) and we are therefore prejudiced. We do not like the natural disappearance of our favourite plants and animals. Then we have to fight nature's way to reinstate those species that support our criteria. Some might say this is a little odd; it certainly seems contrary to the spirit of conservation to be fighting nature. However, this is our only option on such a small island with such a large human population.

By itself a small section of railway, motorway or canal embankment may appear to be insignificant. Taken in the context of the whole network of embankments, it becomes a highly significant habitat for wildlife. They are fine corridors for plant and animal movement along their length. Instead of all being concentrated into one mass, these thin slivers of vegetation offer a life support system for much of our wildlife. That they snake and twist through the British countryside is good, for they pass over many different soil types offering the widest range of habitats for wildlife. Infiltration of wildlife from surrounding habitats is always useful as it adds new species to the existing linear reservoir of wildlife.

Fragmentation of nature reserves is a real possibility when roads or motorways are constructed through them. The worst example is the M40 (London–Oxford) which cuts through the Ashton Rowant National Nature Reserve (NNR). Twenty years after it was done the vegetation still has not established on the chalk cutting. The swathe cut through the nature reserve is so deep and severe that it restricts movement of mammals and many insects. This is a salutory lesson which will hopefully not be repeated with any NNR again. There is also a wind-tunnel effect which restricts animal movement and aids fragmentation. Wherever a motorway passes it always causes irreparable damage to the environment. A three-lane motorway is essentially a nine-lane highway, with two carriageways of three lanes, a central reservation and two verges.

We are always saddened when new roads, motorways and bypasses have to be constructed through virgin countryside. The problems are always with use, whether it is the current problems of the Channel tunnel, the Okehampton bypass through the ancient deer park, the Lyndhurst bypass through the New Forest, the M1 through the ancient battleground of Naseby, the M40 through Britain's best locality for butterflies, the M42 through Lewis Carroll's inspirational countryside for Alice in Wonderland or the M25 through the pretty Darenth Valley in north west Kent. It was an ingenious plan of the Friends of the Earth to divide one threatened site – aptly named Alice's Meadow – into 3,000 lots for sale to members worldwide. This was a headache for the authorities to trace ownership.

Motorway constructors work from a code which helps to produce an aesthetic motorway. Natural features are deliberately designed to be seen readily from the car. In no way does the aesthetic appeal of motorways recompense for the lost mini-habitats, meadows and woodlands which are so useful to the heritage of village communities.

◆ ROADS AND MOTORWAYS ◆

The little lanes of England are a rich haven for Britain's wildlife. The larger roads and dual-carriageways also offer a significant refuge. With over 7,700mi (12,397km) of trunk road in England, Wales and Scotland (1986 figures) this represents a formidable expanse. However, the undisturbed banks of the motorway system are an even better wildlife sanctuary.

Motorways are made up of several different habitats. The grass verges are the principal ones. Then there are the central reservations, little studied by ecologists because of their relative inaccessibility. The hard shoulder is interesting especially at its interface with the grass verge. Here some fascinating food webs are enacted and some very unusual plants grow. So how big is this motorway reserve? The latest figures available from the Department of Transport (the owners of the motorways) are that there are precisely 1,761mi (2,835km) of motorways in England, Scotland and Wales.

Not all motorways have grassy verges and it is estimated that about 40 per cent of them, like the elevated M6 to the east of Birmingham, are without. There is considerable variation in the number of acres of land consumed to make 1mi (1.6km) of motorway under construction. It seems that about 12 acres per mile (4.8ha) is a very modest figure. Twenty acres (8ha) per mile is often quoted as a mean, but the Friends of the Earth state that up to 42a (17ha) per mile may be used. This is certainly not the average figure. They say it is equivalent to thirty-five football pitches.

Using an average of 20a (8ha) of land per mile, then 40 per cent of this is an average of 8a (3.2ha) used. This means that there are about 14,000a. (5,600ha) of grassy motorway verge available for wildlife, on current figures. The significance of this to wildlife is that they have free access to a long thin reserve which, if all squashed up would create a nature reserve about a sixth the size of the Isle of Wight, or 11,666 football pitches, or ten times the size of RSPB Minsmere on the Suffolk coast.

It is perhaps not extraordinary that hundreds of plant species have established themselves along motorway verges, with no help from man. There have been deliberate seeding of interesting species along the M1 and other trunk roads but these have not really blossomed as intended.

One does not see Jacob's ladder, snake's head fritillaries, wild tulip or large bellflower along the M1 although they have been seeded. We do see, however, the bright splashes of corn poppy every time some soil is disturbed on the embankment. This is usually caused by the seed being

brought closer to the surface for germination. There are also yellow patches of primroses, and, increasingly, cowslips which grow as they used to in the countryside long ago. We cannot miss the massed pink blocks of early purple orchids, common spotted orchids, green-winged or pyramidal orchids on banks, though we would be hard pressed to identify them at 70m.p.h. (112km.p.h.).

Poppies are perhaps the most obvious of motorway flowers – a reminder of Flanders field – but there are others. Wild daffodils exploit the banks of the M50, gorse and broom prospers on the sands of the M25.

It is surprising how ordinary roadsides blossom with a riot of orchids. Passed by and unrecognised by most, these roadside orchids are now terribly successful in this refuge. In some cases decapitation at road verge-cutting is not a bad thing for the plants. They still seem to prosper. The only thing they are denied by this rude cutting is a chance to disperse their seed abroad. Some county wildlife trusts have roadside nature reserves.

Cars and juggernauts obviously disperse seed along motorways and roads. One enterprising scientist scrubbed his tyres clean, drove 65mi (105km) in the West Midlands, turned in a few field gateways and hosed down his tyres to collect the seeds. He later germinated thirteen species of plant including 387 seeds of the annual, meadow grass, in a sterile compost.

Movement along any road by man or vehicle will inevitably promote seed dispersal. There have been some interesting ideas put forward on the way various seeds have entered Britain. In Europe the mounted Cossacks probably inadvertently carried seed in their leather straps, the Romans as they marched into England had seeds caught in their leather sandals. Today's man has 'turn-ups' to catch those opportunist seeds, let free miles away from point of collection. How many seeds literally fall off the backs of juggernauts, one day on the continent, the next in England? It is not surprising to find Mediterranean delights such as coriander on our own doorstep.

Grasses are particularly well represented along verges. A few hardy species are planted initially at construction time, but invasive species sometimes (but not always) take over. One third of the British grasses have been found along the M1.

Grand plans were announced in early 1988 to create a nature reserve on a roundabout at Neasden in west London. This is the idea of the London Wildlife Trust who will be creating a wildlife refuge in this urban area. Wild flower meadows, trees and shrubs will surround a man-made pond.

◆ Pollutants

Seaside plants have been very adventurous in recent years. Ardent botanists have tracked them creeping along the roadside verge from coastal areas and on to motorways. So what is going on? Interesting botanical developments were seen first of all in the north-east and south-east. It is all attributed to the colossal amounts of salt we put on roads as de-icers each year. The salt does not go away. The verge becomes more and more salty and the seaside plants love it. They react as if it were an extension of their own habitat. So they creep inland with seed dispersal aided by traffic movement. The interface between the hard shoulder and the verge is very important to them.

We now have sea poas, sea plantain, sea spurrey and sea asters growing in various parts of Britain's motorway system. One can almost imagine sea poas from the south meeting their relatives from the north (by way of the M6 and M56), half way round the M25.

Salt is not the only 'pollutant' which plants (and animals) have to cope with on motorways. There is dust; a significant factor during hot dry weather. Curiously enough wildlife is not really inconvenienced with all the pollutants one finds on motorways. In fact there is more evidence that they prosper than are poisoned. Dust settles on leaves and actually acts as a barrier, below which the heat from the sun's rays collect. Scientists have shown that the internal temperature of the leaf increases in dusty areas adjacent to the road surface and this helps to promote growth. A sort of greenhouse effect. More healthy plant growth occurs, which in turn leads to more insects and birds.

Nickle, cadmium, lead and mercury are the metal pollutants one normally associates with traffic. It becomes incorporated into plants and animals, but does not seem to kill them. Far from it. Nitrogen, another pollutant, accumulates in plant leaves. This stimulates plants to grow and the insect caterpillars which feed on the leaves do better.

Insect populations on motorways verges are booming because of this increased nitrogen input. Buff-tip moths, puss moths, brown-tails and gold-tail moths have all prospered. Some live as large groups of caterpillars and can quickly defoliate their foodplants, such as hawthorn or blackthorn.

Jam-makers look out. There may be 'heavy' wild strawberries and blackberries with doses of lead in them, growing at the edge of a motorway or major road. There will be higher lead levels in market-garden produce grown adjacent to motorways, than away from them, but this is not a serious hazard. If you have the choice always pick blackberries for jam-making in the countryside away from roads. There may be four times less lead in them. You would not want to make 'heavy jam'! If you did, the concentrated levels would still not exceed statutory levels for commercial jam. It is best to avoid roadside blackberries where possible, to lessen any risks.

◆ Birds

The bird most associated with motorways is the kestrel (it's also the symbol of the Young Ornithologists' Club). This bird has benefited greatly from the provision of grassy verges on dual carriageways, roads and motorways. It feeds on small mammals, like mice, shrews and voles. Nothing could be better for these mammals since they enjoy the long lank grass which grows up and falls down year after year providing them with miles of secluded habitat. They have millions of miles of runs below the old grasses and this is their prime habitat. The kestrel keeps a sharp eye out for these animals and swoops to kill any which accidentally break cover. The small mammals are only vermin in urban areas where they sometimes ring bark trees planted on motorway verges. The sight of a kestrel hovering over the carriageway is a familiar sight, frequently around junctions where there is a larger expanse of grass in which its prey lurk. The kestrel really is a versatile bird since it is also found in city centres where it nests on buildings.

The kestrel is a familiar sight near the motorway, hovering on the look-out for small mammals.

Rooks, crows and magpies are common birds along motorways today. They are there as scavengers and even have their nests there. The small woodlands that are now along some of the older parts of the M1 even have rookeries which are very obvious during the winter. During hot weather there is a terrific carnage of small insects on the carriageway. We have all seen how filthy our windscreen becomes on long journeys. Unfortunately honey-bees, bumble-bees, flies and butterflies are windscreen casualties. Those that do not completely disintegrate on the glass, ricochet off and their light bodies are blown to that interesting place, the edge of the hard shoulder. At night the insect mortality continues. Someone has estimated that 1,800 million moths are killed on Britain's roads each year. At first light, the bird scavengers are out cleaning up the insects and squashed mammals.

The rooks, crows and magpies are out on the hard shoulder waiting for the insect hordes to come their way. The insect bodies are blown to the grass verge where they are dismembered and eaten quickly by the ant colonies which line much of this bustling habitat. It has been suggested that the presence of these birds on motorways could be explained by the fact that they ate the earthworms driven up from the ground by rumbling lorries. This cannot be true since most birds are on the hard shoulder and we do not have super-earthworms which penetrate tarmac or concrete. Even the 6ft (1.8m) Australian ones do not have these powers.

A crow devours dead insects which are knocked by cars onto the motorway hard shoulder.

Service stations are also alive with birds. The regulars are chaffinches, sparrows, pied wagtails and of course the larger scavengers. It is surprising how many rookeries there are near the M1's service stations. Birds at service stations take up observation on various strategic high points such as on top of lights. Their sharp eyesight enables them to see any spillage of fast food, bread crumbs or discarded food, and down they come, which acts as a signal to others.

◆ Mammals and amphibians

Much ado has been heard about the carnage of mammals and amphibians on roads. Badgers and foxes are slaughtered in large numbers on newly opened motorways since they have become used to the quiet habitat before the road is opened. After that mortality continues but not at such a high rate.

There are many practical conservation measures in force. On the M3, M5 and M53 there are badger tunnels through which they can trundle unhindered. There are plenty of water culverts, roads and junctions through which these mammals can also pass. A dead badger in February or March is likely to be male since they travel further in search of likely mates than females and expose themselves to greater traffic risks. It is an offence to be found in possession of a badger, even a dead one. If you do find a badger, leave it alone and report it to the Ministry of Agriculture, Fisheries and Food (MAFF).

Foxes do not stick to regular paths like badgers and roam more widely. They are more difficult to control. Wild deer are a real hazard on motorways and two methods have been tried to dissuade them from crossing. Mirrors which reflect headlights of vehicles into adjacent woods have had limited success, but 6ft 6in (2m) high fencing is more suitable.

It is an increasingly common sight to see roadside signs for toad crossings or frog crossings, even swan crossings. As a nation we take a keen interest in our wildlife at a local level and voluntary groups have been eager to reduce the carnage. The Flora and Fauna Preservation Society believe that about $19\frac{1}{2}$ tons (20t) of toads are squashed on our roads each year. To remedy this the first 'toad tunnel' was opened on the A4155 near Henley-on-Thames (Oxfordshire) in March 1987 at a toad black spot. The tunnel is 8in (20cm) in diameter and may help some hedgehogs too. Let's hope this is the beginning of many more animal aids to cross the road.

The case of the fleet-footed hedgehog crossing the road has been successfully debunked by Pat Morris, noted hedgehog expert at London University. Those hedgehogs that roll up spend less time on the move when they could be hit by a tyre. Risk from traffic is not the only problem that hedgehogs have. The high kerb stone may give them some difficulty but they are good climbers. Cattle grids are a big problem though. Once inside hedgehogs are effectively trapped, especially if it is a new grid, since the sides are too high and precipitous for them to climb out. Neglected grids have accumulated soil and leaves allowing an escape route. Now we have a life-saving device which should be fitted into all grids, a hedgehog ladder. Fitted when the grid is first constructed, or added to an existing grid, it is simply a good dollop of concrete at a corner providing a ramp for escape. Such a simple and cheap solution is promulgated by the Hedgehog Preservation Society to which all hedgehog lovers should belong.

◆ RAILWAYS ◆

Britain's railway habitat is about six times more extensive than the motorway system. The lines in current use extend to 11,300 miles (18,193km) and there are about 75,000a (30,000ha) of available space for wildlife.

Grasslands predominate on railways as they do on motorways. There are wastelands at junctions and shunting yards. Cuttings are often rich in wildlife, offering warm south-facing slopes in some cases. The geological formations exposed at cuttings may be more important than the wildlife. Railway verges have had some tree planting to stabilise the soil but it has never been as extensive as that on motorways. Unchecked scrub development on cuttings led to unstable trees toppling in the great storm of October 1987.

There is also the habitat called the 'cess'. This is the drainage area adjacent to the track, which is filled with aggregates, such as gypsum chips. Such a stony habitat is quickly colonised by plants and offers a warm site, with heat radiating off the stones. Colonisation is, though, curtailed by spraying with herbicides. It is along this cess that some casual and unusual plants live.

Some of the more interesting railway land is not just linear. Places like the odd triangles of land nipped off by converging lines, sometimes occupying an acre or so are excellent. Here wildlife prospers in the absence of man. Perhaps the best known example is the Gunnersbury Triangle in west London (Hounslow), a nature reserve of the London Wildlife Trust. It is enclosed by three railway lines (two existing and one redundant) and offers a 6.1a (2.4ha) refuge for urban wildlife. It is a good wildlife resource for children. The subject of massive popular support, the triangle was eventually saved from development.

The lines axed by Lord Beeching in the 1966–7 are a real bonus for nature conservation. Dereliction has done conservation a favour. Wildlife has sprung up along these linear tracks. There is now a proliferation of nature trails and woodland walks along old railway lines, sometimes revitalised with old steam engines. We have the Cuckoo Walk, Primrose Line and Bluebell line in Sussex, the Water-

Speckled wood on bramble leaf.

cress Line in Hampshire and the Ravenglass and Eskdale Railway (locally called the Ratty) in Cumbria which shows off its nature panorama to the public. One Southern Region line, from East Grinstead to Tunbridge Wells is now a linear country park, and a very floristic one at that.

Some of the county wildlife trusts have nature reserves centred around old railway lines. Oxford have the Hook Norton Railway Cutting (19a/7.6ha). In Yorkshire there is the Potteric Carr Nature Reserve and in Nottingham the Kimberley Cutting (12a/4.8ha).

Wherever you find these disused railways they always show off some wildlife delights. Whether it is nightingales singing in the light woodland, chiff-chaffs singing their call, or the willow warbler with its descending scale song. The cuckoo also frequents these wild parts. All four birds are migrants to this country. The old cinder track may have plenty of twayblade orchids, undistinguished in their green hues, but remarkable in their abundance. The base of an embankment may be very wet and supporting both the gaily coloured kingcups (marsh marigolds) or the pink and white cuckoo flower in which the orange tip butterfly takes a lot of interest, as a nectar and caterpillar food source.

Disused stations, where they are still in a state of dereliction after 20 years, make good habitats for wildlife. The stonework is colonised by the wall-rue a delicate native fern of Britain. It much prefers the alkaline mortar between bricks. The introduced but delightful ivy-leaved toadflax, a Mediterranean species grows well on walls. Its tiny seed heads turn into the wall to disperse the seeds in a clever measure to ensure that they reach only those cracks and parts necessary for survival. Wild rose, elder and sloe often grow on the platforms once more accustomed to the trampling of feet. Along the old carriageway discarded apple pips blossom into full-sized apple trees. It is always very interesting to see how the garden flowers, once grown adjacent to the station by old stationmasters proud of their railway gardens, have integrated themselves into the surrounding mass of vegetation. Bulbs, honeysuckle, delphiniums and spiraea can often be found.

Trains have been responsible for the dispersal of at least one plant species throughout the railway network. This was the celebrated Oxford ragwort. It was introduced to the Botanic Garden at Oxford in the mid-eighteenth century, and by 1794 was first seen as an escapee on walls in Oxford. Soon it spread to waste areas and along the pebbly edge of the railway. Used to the stony slopes of Mount Etna in Sicily, its natural home, it found the industrial wastelands a very suitable habitat to colonise. Trains played their part in its dispersal. A story is told by one Claridge Druce, a noted botanist, of how he took a 20m. (32km) train journey in the company of fluffy seeds of Oxford ragwort which also embarked and alighted with him at his destination. The light fluffy seeds were buoyed up in the air and were inadvertently transported by the train on this journey. Railway transport also aided the dispersal of the wall rocket. Whilst railways were reaching out to all corners of the country, new opportunities were being created for plants.

One of the most intensive surveys of railway vegetation ever undertaken, by Caroline Sargent of the Institute of Terrestrial Ecology, has identified over 2,000 species of plants on railway habitats, 70 per cent on cuttings. A nationwide survey has pinpointed 181 British Rail sites which are of outstanding biological interest. Hopefully these will be designated as SSSIs.

It was good news in 1986 to learn that in support of the British Wildlife Appeal, British Rail were giving many interesting biological sites to nature conservation groups. For instance fifty sites were offered to Yorkshire and twenty to groups in Birmingham, Derbyshire, Staffordshire, Warwickshire and Worcestershire amongst many others.

Arguably the railway flora is more diverse than on motorways. This is probably because the railways were constructed before organic herbicides were introduced. This means that wild flower seed was able to colonise the banks freely from surrounding land, to produce the diversity that we see today.

Some of the more common plants can be easily identified from the carriage window. Rosebay willowherb swathes embankments with purple-red flowers in July, giving way to fluffy seed heads. Yellow and cream flowered plants such as the tall mulleins, equally tall melilots and mignonettes are often very much in evidence. The perennial everlasting pea shows off its pink flowers over all that it straddles. Everyone must have seen buddleia and Michaelmas daisies as escapees on embankments, and in urban areas the introduced tree of heaven is common, even in central London.

Two species which have declined somewhat are the convolvulus and and the small toadflax. They rely on early germination of their seed, and the current practice of spring spraying with herbicides probably reduces the chances of these species surviving. In contrast, two annual plants manage to get their growth and reproduction in over winter before herbiciding. These are the whitlow grass and the thale cress.

Rarities such as the alpine lady's mantle, cloudberry and chickweed wintergreen occur on lines throughout the Scottish mountains. Limestone quarries have hoary rockrose, vernal sandwort and Nottingham catchfly (a relation of the white campion, which really does catch flies and lives, amongst other places, in the Nottingham area). Then there is the prostrate toadflax, a rarity in the south-west, meadow saxifrage and Danish scurvy-grass which colonises coastal lines.

Plenty of opportunities are provided by disused railways for insect colonisation. In the Burren in western Eire the orange tip butterfly has used the old railways systems as a corridor for extending its range further into north-east Eire. Other undetected movements have undoubtedly occurred in England and Scotland.

Foxes have traditionally used railways as corridors for penetrating city centres. This was a great opportunity for the light-footed fox to move straight into town via the railway network which went right to the city centre. Numerous observations have been made of foxes tip-toeing over the live line without getting killed. Their fine whiskers must give them some warning.

The badger on the other hand has been less fortunate. Its lumbering gait does not allow it to tip-toe over lines and the carnage has been colossal. Where badgers continue to use traditional paths that cross railways we are likely to have badger mortality. A worrying degree of mortality has been seen in recent years with the electrification of some lines in the south-east. Sixty-eight badgers were killed on the Ashford–Deal line, thirty per 9mi (14.5km) per year in the New Forest, 200 dead along the Maidstone–Ashford line and many more on the electrified Hastings line. All this carnage has alarmed the general public. Fortunately, British Rail has heeded advice and the problem has lessened. Where badgers persistently cross over lines, the electric wires have now been buried underground to make several safe crossing points.

Meadow saxifrage

Marbled white on field scabious.

◆ CANALS ◆

Canals are also significant wildlife corridors. They had their heyday last century carrying industrial traffic when there would have been many more plant introductions attributed to them than now. Many canals have been filled in or lie derelict, but an increasing number are serving a conservation role and are restored, not necessarily for traffic but as wildlife reserves.

Market Harborough prided itself on being the centre of the canal system. One can imagine the canals of England all leading to this area of Leicestershire, man-made corridors ideal for water plants, adventitious bankside weeds and aquatic invertebrates to disperse. One wonders just how many seeds fell from the nose-bags of the horses which used to drag the narrow boats.

London has 50m. (80km) of canals and one of its best is the Regent's park canal, 8½mi (13.5km) long. It feeds the Camley Street Natural Park where many plants and invertebrates associated with canals can be seen. There is even a 'newt trail' to follow. Skullcap and greater water dock are plants found in London along the canal network. Aliens like canary grass and cultivated flax also occur.

Some canal nature reserves are so important that they have been designated as SSSIs. Fourteen miles (22.5km) of the 35mi (56km) long Montgomery canal which runs from Ellesmere (Shropshire) to Newtown in mid-Wales are SSSIs. So too is the Dudley canal, near

Above Disused railway lines make ideal habitats for wildlife. *Below* The black-headed gull (seen here with other species of gull) has prospered since it changed its diet to scavenging.

Netherton in the West Midlands. A speciality of the Montgomery canal is the floating water plantain which is virtually confined to canals in Britain. Other important wildlife canals include the Glamorgan canal, the Wilts and Berks canal, the Great Western canal and the Bridgewater canal at Manchester. It is from there that the National Trust operate narrow boats especially adapted to take the disabled in wheelchairs.

There have been several cases of escaped plants and animals exploiting the waterway system. After all, there are 2,000mi (3,220km) of canal waterways in Britain. Interestingly, the alien plants which have taken to the British canals have been North American.

The Canadian pondweed was first seen in Ireland in 1836, then soon after at Duns Castle (Berwickshire) in 1842. Five years later it was at Market Harborough having been dispersed by boats. The long filaments of Canadian pondweed, break up and establish colonies elsewhere. It is a popular aquarium plant used for aerating tanks, but in the canals there can be too much of it. It clogs up canals and has to be trawled out.

Canadian pondweed is a submerged plant, but a more insidious plant is duckweed which floats on the surface. It is a widely dispersed native which blossoms on canals, ditches and slow-moving streams in the summer and gives that familiar green surface colour indicative of too many agrochemicals in the water. This rich agricultural soup happens to be an ideal growing medium for many canal plants. There are fewer forms of wildlife in an active canal than in a disused one.

Another North American immigrant was the orange balsam. It appeared in Surrey in 1822 and within 20 years was dispersed along the Grand Union Canal and in Middlesex and Hertfordshire. It is now a widely dispersed alien along canals and rivers in Britain.

A favourite in garden ponds is the water fern with the delightful Latin name of *Azolla*. Like duckweed it is a free-floating plant, and will go wherever the wind takes it. Blooms of it build up on waterways and ponds, first a delicate green colour, then attractive autumn tints of reddish-brown and copper. Unfortunately it has contributed to the clogging-up problems of some canals such as the Grand Western, where a dense green mat of *Azolla* over a mile long has built up in the past.

Where warm water exists along canals in urban areas and alongside factories, the water is suitable for freshwater invertebrates and fish to prosper. There are true tales of goldfish and guppies thriving in warm spots and of various North American crustacean shrimps (with Latin names only) taking to British waterways. In more recent years, a troublesome exotic crab, the Chinese mitten crab, has turned up in the River Thames and in Regent's Canal. It has already reached Yorkshire and could become a menace since it can undermine banks when it burrows using its large 'mitten' claws.

In unpolluted waters, especially in unused canals the potential for recreational fishing is great. In fact in still canal water it is a real pleasure to watch the fish, something which is impossible to do in the churned-

Churchyards are very rich in flora and fauna.

Small skipper on hawkbit.

up waters of an active canal. The fish most often found in canal waters are roach, perch, bream, tench and pike. There are plenty of freshwater insects, caddis flies, mayflies and alderflies to feed on. Dragonflies are always a good indicator of biologically-rich sites. Twenty-six species along a stretch of waterway is a good figure to aim for, but often fewer are recorded these days.

Canal bank vegetation offers refuges for insects and small mammals, providing the vegetation is not grubbed-out or grazed-off, which often happens in improved lowland or on grade 1 soil. The emergent and semi-emergent vegetation is essential as hiding places, resting places and hatching posts for aquatic insects. In the south-west of England and in Scotland otters frequent the water's edge only where there is adequate cover. Look out for their spraints, or droppings, along the river or canal's edge. Banks of sand in sheltered spots may be chosen by kingfishers as nesting sites. In contrast dippers often choose to nest behind thick ivy on a weir, waterfall or building, frequently in places associated with man. Both interesting species are noted as urban birds, passing through city centres via the waterways, often unnoticed and undisturbed by man.

WILDLIFE SANCTUARIES

We continue the theme of 'reservoirs' for wildlife from the last chapter. There are several other places in our 'countryside' which blossom with wildlife apart from the unofficial linear nature reserves of our roads, railways and canals.

What so amazes naturalists is that wildlife has the uncanny ability to colonise all sorts of man-made habitats. Whatever new habitats are generated by man some animals and plants will find a home there. Frequently it will be only a few species which will prosper, the opportunist ones which can cope with these new ecological regimes and habitats, of say, non-stop fluorescent lighting and hot tin roofs.

Here we look at wildlife in towns, churchyards, wasteland, golf courses and Ministry of Defence land. From the plant and animal point of view these are genuine extensions of their own habitats, indeed it may be their only habitats. Life in the 'real' countryside is perhaps unknown and 'foreign' to say the least. Gregarious man has built his own concrete catacombs to live in, and at the same time provided an extensive playground for animals and sanctuary for wild flowers. The surface area of habitats available for wildlife in urban areas is dramatically increased and ripe for colonisation. No wonder wildlife abounds there.

Wildlife conservation in urban areas goes on along two fronts, passive and active. Wildlife thrives wherever man lives simply because it is adequately, and inadvertently, provided for by suitable nooks and crannies. Active conservation is steaming ahead via the work of voluntary conservation bodies. Some urban wildlife groups are more active than those in the 'real' countryside.

· TOWNS AND CITIES ·

There are great advantages to wildlife of living in towns and cities. It is much warmer – sometimes about 40°F (5°C) warmer – than living in the country. To a plant this gives it an extra 3 weeks growing period over the year than its contemporaries out of town. There are reduced numbers of nights without frost, occasionally no frost at all in some cities, insulated from bad weather by radiation from buildings and pavements and warmth from rivers. There are more hotter days in towns, and in London the climate can approach that of the Mediterranean.

For commuters coming into town the effects of this warmer climate can be seen readily. Bushes coming into flower 2–3 weeks earlier than in the country. On the negative side fewer and fewer lichens are seen on rooftops nearer the city centre because aerial pollution kills them off.

Certain birds are not put off by concrete jungles, indeed they may prefer them. Our high rises are like artificial cliffs, safe from predators on the outside. The kestrel frequently nests on office ledges much to the amazement and excitement of city workers. It's an adaptable bird quite at home in the countryside or, as most frequently seen, hovering over our motorway verges.

Kittiwakes nest gregariously on narrow ledges provided by factories in certain towns in the north-east. Normally they find secure places on cliffs. In Aberdeen, oystercatchers – the residents call them 'oycs' – nest on the pebble-dash roofs in the city. In our design of flat-topped roofs so often seen in municipal buildings such as schools, libraries and office buildings we have imitated the wide expanses of coastal shell beach where these birds would normally nest. The 'oycs' have also taken to nesting on North Sea gas pumping stations along some of the pumping routes.

Another artificial cliff-dweller is the black redstart, a Mediterranean bird, which finds the office window ledge, or the ledge of power stations ideal for nesting purposes. This bird is very rare in the countryside and best found in urban areas.

Schools with large expanses of recreational ground offer a green haven for seabirds, a safe haven for resting during high tide or for feeding. Aberdeen has had rarities such as ivory gulls and glaucous gulls on lawns. Waxwings are winter visitors which can sometimes strip the cotoneaster and whitebeam berries.

Redshanks have changed their life style to suit the urban environment. Normally this is a coastal bird but in some areas it now roosts on roofs of buildings and goes night feeding on recreational grounds thanks to municipal lighting. It also frequents sewage works.

There are over a hundred seaside towns in Britain which are plagued by the herring gull, an opportunist scavenger. Over 3,000 urban pairs have been recorded. This raucous gull nests amongst chimney pots and can become a nuisance particularly for the authorities. Pied wagtails flock together in groups of over a thousand in some areas and roost on factory roofs. Normally they are found in very small groups in the countryside and make a good job of cleaning up flies around farm buildings.

Owls about town are more frequent than you may suppose, since they are nocturnal. Where the suburbs are full of trees and where there are mature parks and gardens there are adequate habitats available for the native tawny owl and the introduced little owl from Italy, a common

Primrose

suburban species. They are useful birds since they eat all sorts of insects, many of them pests.

Parks and gardens also offer refuge for escaped parakeets which manage to survive the winter and now live in several areas in large flocks, with over 100 individuals. Feral pigeons, starlings and sparrows are so much more successful. Britain's winter population of starlings reaches a staggering 35 million including migrants. There was once a grand scheme of 'depigeonisation' in Paris to rid it of its 15,000 pairs of pigeons by introducing several pairs of peregrin falcons. Successful use of peregrins has been achieved at Berlin airport however.

Conservation groups put up bird boxes which is always a good thing to increase density. Bird boxes should face north, bat boxes south since chicks will not roast in the sun, and bats can derive as much heat as possible. Those who like to encourage hedgehogs – another beneficial animal – may like to erect hedgehog hibernation shelters. These are simply pieces of wood leant against a wall or garden shed and lightly stuffed with dry grass. This dry hibernation quarters will be readily used by hedgehogs. Mammals are nearly always welcome in gardens, especially the dormouse. It too can be encouraged with an artificial nest, though it may decide to choose a tit box to hibernate in. A nest for a dormouse can be made from an old tennis ball. A 1in (2.5cm) hole, the size of a tit-box hole, is cut in the ball and the ball is then mounted on a post which is then secured in the hedge.

Bats have caught the imagination of amateur naturalists in the last 10 years in a way that could not have been imagined previously. These small furry mammals are all now protected under the Wildlife & Countryside Act of 1981. There are fifteen resident species and several of these frequent the attics of new houses. Species like the small pipistrelle, the brown long-eared, Daubenton's, natterer's bat and whiskered bat are found in houses. Each pipistrelle may eat about 3,500 insects every evening it goes out hunting, doing us all a favour as a pest controller. Cavity walls and attics are entered by bad-fitting soffits and offer refuges for these nocturnal animals.

Regional bat groups help to promote the cause of bats. There has been a phenomenal growth of interest in bats, from twenty-three bat groups in 1984 to over seventy in 1988. The greatest threat to bats is the treatment of timber, whose toxic fumes and chemicals soon kill them. Over 100,000 properties are treated annually and fortunately there is

Protected by the 1981 Wildlife & Countryside Act,
the bat is an efficient pest controller.

now more liaison between treatment companies, local bat groups and local trusts. There have been fines for offenders. Disturbing bats in their roosts can upset them. The law states that it is illegal to 'kill, injure or handle any bat'. It is best to have professional help or seek advice from a local bat group or wildlife trust.

Badgers are more often welcome in gardens than unwelcome. They do sometimes turn up the lawn or flower bed looking for grubs and bulbs and they may excavate a spoil heap over the corner of the garden if their 'earth' – their living quarters – is adjacent to the garden. However, they are friendly mammals which are often actively encouraged to come for night feeding sessions by enthralled conservationists. Instead of earthworms and bulbs many urban badgers eat pork pies and pasties. A recent survey suggested that there might be about 216,000 badgers in Britain, based on an average of six badgers in each of the 36,000-odd setts.

Foxes are equally tolerated in the garden, their only problem is that they like to rummage through the contents of the dustbin. There have been various studies on urban foxes. One, conducted by junior members of WATCH in 1983 recorded over 1,300 foxes in London. Throughout the country there are thought to be 252,000, that is the spring adult fox population estimated in 1981. In the country, foxes require more space to live and support a family than in the town. Territory sizes of city foxes living in Oxford for example are about 99a (40ha) compared to about 578a (234ha) in the country.

Feral cats are a nuisance in some towns and cities and have to be vigorously controlled. 'Feeders', or people who decide to feed cats – and there are many cat-lovers – allow cats to exist in a smaller area than they would normally as food is abundant. In the countryside a tom cat may exercise control over an area of 150–200a (60–80ha). The town tom will have a range of about a tenth of this, or sometimes just a twentieth.

Urban wildlife can be full of surprises. Britain may not have had the 6ft 6in (2m) long crocodile which was found in the drains of Paris, an escapee which had done well eating rats, but in parts of Gloucester in 1988 it was raining pink frogs! This curious episode may be explained by the tiny Saharan pink frogs being borne on strong winds with the Saharan dust all the way to Gloucester.

If you like wildlife, towns are pretty good places to live in. You may not have the green grass, scenic views and the farmyard cock, but your garden may be full of butterflies and your garden pond overflowing with amphibians. Some intrepid wildlifers have even put green grass on their rooftops, fenced it in, and put a small flock of sheep up there to keep it down. Very green, ecological and organic!

◆ CHURCHYARDS AND CEMETERIES ◆

Close to most communities there are either churchyards or cemeteries. Both are reservoirs for wildlife and their cumulative area nationwide is of considerable benefit to wildlife. In Ceredigion (formerly Cardigan-shire) about 75 per cent of all churchyards are interesting biologically. Churchyards are generally older than cemeteries.

The great ecological importance of churchyards is that they may have been simply unimproved church (or glebe) land enclosed for burial purposes and have changed little since. They are ancient meadows put to another use. Apart from minimal management they may have totally escaped any interference from chemicals.

It is to churchyards and cemeteries that botanists, lichenologists, entomologists and mammalogists amongst others, turn for the chance of making exciting discoveries. There are always delights to offer naturalists, amateur and professional, in town or country. Whether it is interested bat groups studying the bats in the belfry, lepidopterists looking at butterflies and moths in the churchyard or sylviculturalists studying the trees, churchyards are incredibly rich in flora and fauna.

Trees are always worth a second look in churchyards. Often planted in respect of the dead they become old, gnarled, hollow, split and perfect for wildlife in all its diversity. It is even better in overgrown or disused cemeteries where wildlife prospers. Some cemeteries are now nature reserves, like the Nunhead cemetery (52a/21ha) in south-west London. It is a paradise for foxes and birds such as the wren, pigeons and blackbirds. The famous Highgate Cemetery was originally established as 100a (40ha) and much of it has now been taken over by trees. Sycamores and ash have pushed tombs apart revealing plenty of hiding places for small and large mammals.

Yew is a familiar tree in churchyards and there are plenty of reasons proposed for its presence there. First, it was natural to plant yew in respect of the dead. It is a symbol of longevity. After all it *is* the oldest growing tree in Britain. Many are over 1,000 years old, such as those at Dover (Kent), Tisbury (Wiltshire) and Crowhurst (Surrey). The oldest is in a churchyard at Fortingall on Loch Tay (Perthshire), possibly over 1,500 years old. As yews age they tend to split and look as though they are several specimens. Second, yew makes a good wind-screen. Take note, it is frequently planted against the prevailing wind. Victorians did not like their hats blowing off on the way to church! Yew's evergreen needles give colour through the winter as well as being an efficient wind-break. Third, yew's wood is very flexible and it was prized for the making of staves. However, it is thought that taller growing Normandy yews provided better staves than the squatter English trees. As yew was so useful it had to be grown in the churchyard since the fruits are poisonous (that is, the central greenish part only) and livestock had to be kept away from them. There is more sense in growing the Irish yew in churchyards since its straight cathedral-like sides reach up to heaven.

The wildlife associated with yew is fairly limited. Very few plants grow under yew since the needles are resinous, unpalatable to insects and the thick canopy of the tree excludes light from the ground. Oaks and limes which are popular trees in churchyards are much better. They harbour hundreds of different insect species. The more insects the more insectivorous birds can be expected, even greater and lesser spotted woodpeckers. Limes are often 'pleached' in uniform avenues. This is an old practice of training the limbs to the side or as an arch, and cutting back each year. There is only one variety of lime which does not have those awful aphids on them which are responsible for those sugary secretions which falls out of the trees in mid-summer. It's called *Tilia* × *euchlora*.

Trees in churchyards or cemeteries always look good. We in Britain, rarely indulge in the practice of planting funeral cypress (otherwise called the pencil cedar or Mediterranean cypress) which fingers its way up to heaven – as a mark of respect to the dead. This is very much a Mediterranean habit. Scot's pine and strawberry trees may have been secretely planted in English churchyards as some sort of signal to others that Jacobite sympathies were tolerated. A wide variety of conifers is often found in churchyards.

Churchyards and cemeteries are incredibly rich in lichens. This is because one group of lichens, the ones which live on stones, are well catered for. The variety of headstones and tombs provides them with a wide variety of different chemical substrates. Lichens are particular as to where they live. Many more will be found on limestones, than on sandstone, granite or slate. Polished stone is a poor substrate. The aspect, either north or south is important too. Over eighty lichen species have been recorded from some parishes in Britain, though the record is about 180 from Mickleham churchyard in Surrey.

Lichen species are generally very difficult to sort out. Many look the same grey or greenish colour. Others though are bright and are easier to determine. They are all slow growers, putting on only $\frac{1}{10}$in (1–2mm) each year to their roundish growths. Lichens look a little fungus-like.

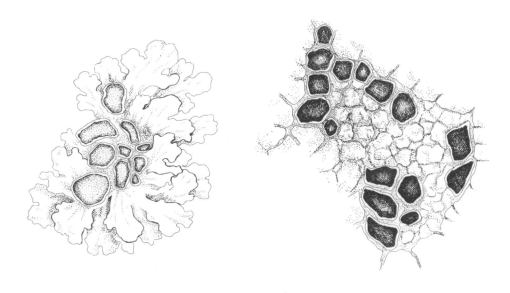

Churchyards and cemeteries are rich in lichens like these two (left) Xanthoria parietina, *and* (right) Lecanora atra.

There is good reason for this since they are made up of half fungus and half algae. They can be used for some degree of dating but sometimes the substrate peels off and the process starts all over again. Some lichens like the chemical nutrients which run off headstones, especially those nitrogenous ones deposited there by perching birds. They enrich the stone and make a different sort of habitat for some discerning lichens.

The wild flowers of churchyards are remarkable. Small churchyards may have over a hundred species. There are many national or local rarities found in churchyards. Snowdrops, daffodils, buttercups and oxeye daisies may be abundant in the spring, cow parsley in the summer. There are churchyards studded with orchids, of many species, rare tall thrift, snake's head fritillaries and wallflowers.

Introduced species, naturalised in churchyards are common and often owe their place to the enthusiasm of itinerant parson-naturalists of the last century. Some of these plants are attractive. The Italian *Anemone appenina* rubs its delicate blue shoulders with the white wood anemone or windflower, which nods its blossom around in the spring air. The yellow winter aconites also look attractive. Japanese knotgrass and rhododendrons may be a problem though.

The diversity of wild flowers in churchyards is attributed to there not being any herbiciding. A balance has to be maintained in the management of churchyards and cemeteries between allowing them to get out of hand and thick in brambles, and having a neat and tidy site. In some cases churchyards are cleaned up by removing headstones to the edge. This should be avoided if at all possible since it eliminates many lichens. Cutting the hay in churchyards is best done in late June or July when all the grasses have flowered, fruited and dispersed their seed. Grazing with sheep or goats is ideal, cost effective and organic.

There has been much interest shown in the flora and fauna of churchyards in recent years, thanks mainly to Francesca Greenoak's book *God's Acre*. The Prince of Wales committee convened a seminar on Graveyards and the Environment in 1982, and many groups became involved in the nationwide survey of the flora of churchyards organised by the Botanical Society of the British Isles. Over the last 7 years members of the Norfolk Naturalists' Trust have run a Churchyard Conservation Scheme and now look after 100 of their best churchyard nature reserves.

◆ GOLF COURSES ◆

Golf courses have always been good places for wildlife and they are now helping to protect some of Britain's rarer species. In fact there is now a Golf Course Wildlife Trust which co-ordinates information. Older, well established golf courses are better than the newer ones which try to re-create woodlands and 'rough' areas with exotic trees and acres of rye grass.

The reason for the importance of golf courses is that they have often been built on marginal land such as grassland or heathland and now harbour certain forms of plants and animals otherwise driven out from the surrounding urban or developed land. The 'rough' is the best part for wildlife, not for golfers. The amount of available land represented by golf courses nationally makes a significant wildlife reservoir.

There are over 2,200 golf courses in Britain and collectively they represent about 268,292a (107,316ha). This is calculated on an average sized, 18-hole course of 122a (48ha). The 'rough' represents about 60 per cent of the whole. When these figures are compared with the 390,244a (156,097ha) of National Nature Reserves designated in Britain, we see that golf courses represent about two thirds of this, a significant reservoir.

It is fortuitous that wildlife still likes golf courses. Much can be said for courses which are established on old dune systems or along cliff tops. In their own way they protect these rich habitats and make them unavailable to other coastal recreations which are far more deleterious, such as caravans, housing, tourism and other recreational facilities.

On chalky grassland orchids grow prolifically. At the famous Royal St George at Sandwich Bay (Kent) the best colony of lizard orchid occurs. Golfers are issued with an explanatory leaflet indicating the botanical treasures of the 'rough'. It also has the best British populations of a parasitic plant, the bedstraw broomrape and is the only Kent locality for a certain rare moss.

There are great crested newts on the unimproved meadows of the Hylands Park golf course (Essex), natterjack toads on the old sand dunes of the Royal Liverpool (Cheshire) and dune gentians at Tenby (west Wales). The course at St Andrews (Scotland) offers refuge to migrant birds and there are butterflies galore on many other grassland golf courses.

So the next time you go onto the golf course look out for wild flowers, insects and birds. The skylark is a familiar bird of the rough. It's also a refuge for badgers and foxes which will also breed there.

◆ WASTELAND ◆

Urban environments have a variety of wastelands. These may be as a result of industrial workings such as spoil heaps, or through urban dereliction. There is some floristic similarity with railways since the ecology of sidings, cesses and marshalling yards is similar to areas of derelict land.

One of the most famous of urban wasteland sites was the William Curtis Ecological Park, originally a 2a (0·8ha) site on the south side of Tower Bridge in London, opposite Traitor's Gate. It demonstrated superbly what can be done with small urban sites that are perhaps waiting for re-development, in, say 2, 4 or 10 years time. Students at the park saw what could be done in a short time. Quick-growing trees could be planted, an artificial pond built, a mini-dune system created so that inner-city students didn't have to travel out of town to see ecological wonders.

The park was created in 1976 from sub-soil and blossomed almost immediately. Within a few years 270 species of wild plant were found there, two-thirds getting there by their own means of wind dispersal. One hundred and sixty species of insect were recorded and thirty-five species of bird. Kestrels which nested on Tower Bridge combed the park for small mammals. Waterfowl and amphibians arrived at the artificial pond. Foxes trotted through this successful urban reserve.

Quarries and soil heaps both make excellent sanctuaries for wildlife. There are probably more than 100 quarries which are now scheduled as SSSIs. Many are stiff with the early purple or common spotted orchids in the spring. If the aggregate mined or spoil heap material is at all alkaline then this provides an ideal habitat for orchids. Orchids like the soil alkaline (or pH 7–14) and alkali dumps serve them very well. Chalk and sand which has originated from ground up (calcareous) sea shells high in calcium are ideal mediums for orchid germination. Some problems arise when old quarries are used for landfill and populations of wild plants or butterflies suffer.

Wherever the land is left vacant there are great opportunities for introduced wild plants to prosper. Often this is at the expense of native plants, but the effect can sometimes be quite beautiful. One of the pioneers of wasteland is buddleia, whose long blue spikes attract insects, particularly butterflies in great numbers. It is rightly called the butterfly bush. Then there is the yellow-flowered Oxford ragwort (actually from Sicily), and policemen's helmets, otherwise called Himalayan balsam. Not all introduced wasteland plants are necessarily beautiful or wanted.

Perhaps one of the prettiest introduced plants is Thanet cress. A casual along roadsides, it was inadvertently brought into this country (through Ramsgate in Kent) as a filling for stuffed mattresses. Wounded campaigners were brought back on foreign mattresses and when these

Common spotted orchid.

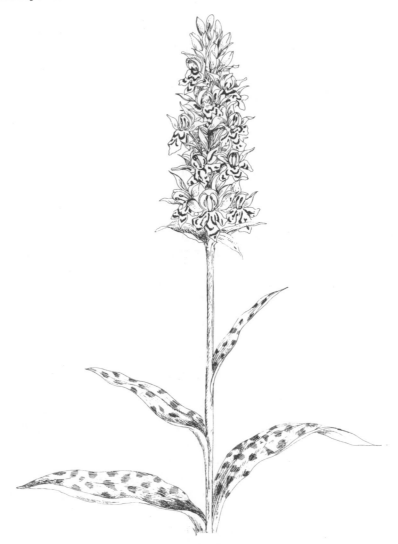

were dispensed with the hay stuffing was turned on to the local farmland in Thanet. Thus Thanet cress spread in Britain through this unlikely means and colonises roadside verges and wasteland.

Not all introduced plants are necessarily beautiful or have such colourful history. The Japanese knotgrass is a miserable pest, a pernicious weed along roadsides and on wasteland.

Several escapees from gardens have made their way on to wasteland, lupins, monbretia, winter heliotrope and rhododendrons can make naturalised strands of vegetation. Rhododendrons are pests when they grow in the wrong place and ruin woodlands, ousting most other species in their hideous advance – a conservationist's nightmare.

Establishment of vegetation on spoil tips is difficult to effect, though frequently attempted. The problem arises from the tip site having such a steep angle, the result of storing so much material in a limited area. Erosion is the main problem. Where terracing and seeding is possible remarkable greening of the spoil material often occurs. Otherwise, spoil heaps do sprout irregularly with their own range of wild plants, such as viper's bugloss, common ragwort, willowherb, mignonette, sallow, sycamore, silver birch all of which support plenty of insects.

◆ LANDFILL SITES AND ◆ SEWAGE FARMS

'Shoddy' was responsible for the introduction of many wild grasses into this country. This was a waste product of the wool industry and the little knots of wool often containing seeds, were discarded on the fields. At least 200 species of grass were introduced into Britain via shoddy. On a wider scale it is not surprising that about one third of wild plants on the British list are introduced species, brought in by a variety of means, active and passive. Today, rubbish tips have taken on the non-exclusive role of many plant introductions, some of them surprises.

Cannabis, or hemp, is a species which turns up occasionally on rubbish dumps. Its route here is via the discarded budgerigar soil tray, along with sunflower, canary grass and fuller's teasel.

Britain has a major problem of disposing of its own rubbish, let alone other people's rubbish, such as that from the USA which threatened various British sites. Britain produces enough municipal rubbish each year to bury the Isle of Wight all over to a depth of about a yard. About 147 tons (150,000t) of rubbish are produced by a city with half a million people.

Much of this rubbish is filled into old quarry working sites, occasionally into narrow valleys, much to the distress of naturalists. Incineration can be a productive investment, returning electricity to the national grid from the combustion. Edmonton in north London produces £4.5 million per year by burning all its rubbish. Over fifty incinerators are now in use in Britain.

About 85 per cent of Britain's rubbish is used as landfill. At least 2.45 million tons (2.5 million t) of glass are now recycled. Cheshire County Council was faced with the problem of finding places to dump its 1.2 million tons of rubbish each year. It had to encroach upon an interesting SSSI site, but this led to an ingenious 'creative conservation scheme'. Research demonstrated that it was possible to reinstate the lime-bed vegetation on to raw, unweathered lime-waste. The 8-year scheme, active during the working life of the site, will provide a nature reserve on the original infill site.

Another successful landfill site which has been designed to be a public amenity is Martin's farm, near Colchester (Essex). When the working life of the landfill was finished 18in (0.6m) of topsoil was put over the site. Leachate was contained so that it did not affect the nearby coastal SSSI marshes and experimental plantings were carried out. Ninety per cent vegetational cover was achieved within 4 years, using amenity plants like oxeye daisy and cowslip, butterfly nectar plants like knapweed and hawbit, and caterpillar food plants like bird's foot trefoil and lady's smock. All was a great success since eighteen species of butterfly were recorded on the site, including five species which breed on grasses. So far there are 143 species of wild plant recorded.

Both the herring gull and the black-headed gull owe a great deal to rubbish dumps for their well-being. The black-headed gull has prospered since it changed its diet to scavenging through rubbish. Now it is a highly successful species often found well inland. Their presence on rubbish dumps, together with rooks, crows and jackdaws is typical. They follow the rubbish carts, even responding to the bleeped danger note that reversing carts make just prior to discharging a load. The birds appear to materialise from nowhere.

Where water collects on waste ground, roadsides or on rubbish dumps there is an interesting tiny creature called a fairy shrimp which may survive there. It lives in and lays its eggs in, little pools of water. If the puddle dries up then the eggs stay in a dormant stage until it rains again. The development of the shrimp then continues. Usually about $\frac{1}{16}$in (1mm) long fairy shrimps are found in the wild and on many man-made habitats in southern England.

Sewage treatment works offer opportunities for both birds and birders. Birds flock to sewage farms because of the super-abundance of flies. Regular breeding birds at sewage farms are moorhen, pied wagtail and reed bunting. Mallard, sedge warbler and yellow wagtail are frequently found. People interested in birds go to sewage farms often to get their first taste of ornithology. Sewage farms are not always too far from urban areas and offer opportunities to see common birds as well as interesting visitors.

Summer visitors to individual sewage farms have reached forty-four species. Short-eared owls may be seen as well as the green sandpiper. So important is the food at sewage works to ruffs and green sandpipers that it has helped to increase their populations. Where extensive sludge lagoons are used, as in Nottingham, very large populations of lapwings (40,000) and golden plovers (3,000) have been recorded scavenging.

◆ MOD RESERVOIRS ◆

One of the most significant of reservoir sites for British wildlife is now on Ministry of Defence (MOD) property. The MOD own 682,000a

(272,800ha). What might wildlife be doing on such apparently disrupted sites you may well ask. The answer is that not all MOD land is intensively used. Conservation is taken very seriously by the military. They have a band of 5,000 citizens, both military and civilian who watch over wildlife nationwide. Records have been pouring in since 1973 when Lt Col C. N. Clayden MBE (Ret'd) took up the position of conservation officer for the MOD. He has masterminded conservation on MOD sites for 16 years. This was at a time when many other influential governmental or quasi-governmental organisations didn't have conservation officers at all.

Wildlife thrives on MOD land for various reasons. First, the general public are excluded. This is good news for wildlife since the depredations felt from man-the-picker-trampler-and-collector are spared. It does not matter than 18,000 soldiers pass through some sites on manoeuvres, they are concentrated in small areas. Second, the relatively large size of the MOD holdings allows for superb populations of animals and plants to build up undisturbed. Third, MOD's voluntary band of conservationists actively manage wildlife so that it prospers even more.

In 1988 MOD signed a Declaration of Intent with the Nature Conservancy Council (NCC) to look after wildlife on their sites, national defence being the primary role. There are many SSSIs of biological, geological and archaeological interest on MOD property and the MOD now undertake to look after these sites sympathetically. Nature conservation will be incorporated into their management strategies.

It is quite amazing how much of Britain's wildlife is present on MOD land. In several cases there are bigger, better populations of plants or animals on some MOD sites, than comparable areas of countryside elsewhere. Their list of 'best of British' sites makes any conservationist cringe with envy.

The MOD have the best bat locality in Britain with ten of the fifteen bat species present. There is an area of grassland with an incredible antscape of three million ant hills, a natural habitat with 18,000 juniper bushes (Porton Down), the best butterfly site in Britain with forty-five species (Porton Down), the best dragonfly and damselfly site with twenty-four species and the only site in Britain where all twelve reptiles and amphibians can be found. It is a good thing that the general public are excluded from these sites and that first-rate semi-natural habitats and their attendant wildlife are conserved.

Porton Down on the Wiltshire/Hampshire border is a phenomenal place biologically. It has the largest area of chalk grassland in the country. With its wide range of butterfly species present it is filled with a myriad of native and immigrant butterflies by the autumn. Reports of driving across the Down in September describe nil visibility with so many dark green fritillaries and marbled white butterflies. There are

---

Above left Urban allotments and golf courses provide diverse habitats for wildlife. *Above right* The William Curtis Ecological Park pioneered urban conservation. *Below* Britain's most southerly ESA is the West Penwith area of Cornwall.

fifteen other MOD sites which have more than thirty species of butterfly present. These include Greenham Common (Berkshire), Aldermaston (Berkshire), Farnborough (Hampshire), Lulworth (Dorset) and West Dean (Wiltshire).

There is an Army Bird Watching Society which has ringed 54,000 birds of 146 species since 1978. Quite a feat for eighty-five MOD banders. Wetland sites like the Wash (now of international importance) offer refuge to waders as well as marine mammals. The highest percentage of breeding birds of the stone curlew, Dartford warblers, cirl bunting, little tern, chough, hobby, wheatear, gadwall and nightjar breed exclusively on MOD land. Hen harriers and short-eared owls are attracted to many MOD sites.

Wild flowers are prolific on MOD lands and add a great deal of colour. Botanists at Stanford (Norfolk) recorded 637 species of plant, thirty-two of which were rare or uncommon. There are just as many at Farnborough too. The best sites in Britain for maiden pink, grape hyacinth, coral root orchid, tree mallow and purple milk vetch occur on MOD land.

Cowslip

Above Unfortunately, activities such as motorbike scrambling are still allowed in some of Britain's finest countryside. *Below* At Thorney Island, sailing and wildlife conservation exist harmoniously side by side.

INTERPRETATION

As we all become more aware of conservation we start to use its language. The public at large are confronted with information centres, interpretive centres and park centres wherever they go and the press is often full of the conservation jargon. All this is in a successful bid to proliferate information and to educate. Conservation *is* succeeding.

To recent converts to conservation, how do they pick up the threads? The natural world seems to be full of SSSIs and AONBs, NNRs and ESAs. Conservationists seem to be great splitters, partitioning the land into its particular (and peculiar) habitats. This patchwork of Britain's conserved land needs some disentangling and interpretation for the uninitiated. It also needs some unravelling for the initiated who are perhaps unaware that SSSIs were designated over 40 years ago. This chapter attempts to establish the meaning of some of those definitions.

· CONSERVATION ACRONYMS ·

Any alien to the world of conservation would feel understandably confused. Conservationists speak a language of their own. National and local papers dwell on the rape of the countryside and point to the disappearance of SSSIs, thus perpetuating this conservation language. So what are all these acronyms? The list below hopefully helps you through the plethora of names and initials used in conservation circles. Many have been mentioned either in the text or in the Further Information section where contact details are given (see pages 151–6).

Some conservation groups, like Greenpeace do not appear on the list of acronyms as they have just one name. Friends of the Earth do. Name changes which reflect changes in conservation thinking or give added weight to the respectability of an organisation, alter some acronyms. For instance, BASC used to be WAGBI (Wildfowlers of Great Britain and Ireland); the RSNC used to be the STNC (Society for Nature Conservation) and some county wildlife trusts have changed their names to Trust for Wildlife Conservation, e.g. STNC (Sussex Trust for Nature Conservation) to Sussex Wildlife Trust. All this adds to the confusions. The most recent change has been the WWF, now no longer the familiar World Wildlife Fund, but the World Wide Fund for Nature, keeping the same initials.

ACRIMONIUS
·ACRONYMS·

ADAS	Agricultural Development and Advisory Services	FWAG	Farming and Wildlife Advisory Group
AONB	Area of Outstanding Natural Beauty	FC	Forestry Commission
BASC	British Association for Shooting and Conservation	GC	Game Conservancy
BBCS	British Butterfly Conservation Society	LNR	Local Nature Reserve
BSBI	Botanical Society of Great Britain and Europe	MAFF	Ministry of Agriculture, Fisheries and Food
BTO	British Trust for Ornithology	MOD	Ministry of Defence
BR	British Rail	NCC	Nature Conservancy Council
CEGB	Central Electricity Generating Board	MNR	Marine Nature Reserve
CPRE	Council for the Protection of Rural England	NNR	National Nature Reserve
CC	Church Commissioners County Council Countryside Commission Crown Commissioners	NT	National Trust
		RSNC	Royal Society for Nature Conservation
		RSPB	Royal Society for the Protection of Birds
ESA	Environmentally Sensitive Areas	SSSI	Sites of Special Scientific Interest
FOE	Friends of the Earth	WFS	Wild Flower Society
		WWF	World Wide Fund for Nature
		WT	Woodland Trust

Interpreting the countryside is a necessary skill for nature conservation. It is useful to be able to recognise a habitat from a distance. This is done by reading the type of flora growing there. The flora is determined by the geology and aspect, so if you know what sort of soil you are on, the type of habitat growing there can be predicted. The original habitat of course will not be present, but a 'secondary habitat' may be present, or the area may have been 'improved' by agriculture. It is useful to remember that oak tends to grow on clay, beech on chalk and silver birch on sands and gravels.

Virtually all of the lowland countryside of southern England is regarded as 'semi-natural'. This means that the original 'natural' habitat has gone and in its place has grown up a replacement vegetation. Much of the replacement vegetation reflects the suite of species once found in the natural habitat. The semi-natural habitats of which we are all very familiar, which makes up the patchwork of typical English landscape has been managed by man. This could all be loosely called secondary vegetation. In fact the woods and copses with which you are familiar may have grown up, been felled and regenerated many times since the original wood was felled; not just the second (or 'secondary') time.

An intermediary stage in nature regeneration of woodland habitats is scrub. Now many people are confused by what scrub is. It is not a particular plant species. It can be a variety of different species all jostling to establish themselves on the previously felled or grubbed out habitat. On chalky soils it may well be spindle, guelder rose, wayfaring tree,

whitebeam, wild clematis and wild raspberry. On clay it may be hawthorn, blackthorn (sloe), briar and honeysuckle. Scrubby commons and wastelands are invaluable habitats for wildlife, the bushes providing song posts for birds, the grassy areas providing sanctuary to butterflies and grasshoppers and any bare ground to lizards and snakes.

• MARINE NATURE RESERVES (MNRs) •

Britain's coastline is scattered with many rich habitats for marine wildlife. Until recently Britain has lagged behind many other countries in establishing Marine Nature Reserves (MNRs). France, Italy, Ireland and the Nordic countries have all established marine nature reserves. New Zealand, the size of Great Britain, established its first reserve in 1977 and there are many lessons to be learnt in how they overcame problems.

So what are the problems that have made us slow at establishment? The answer lies in the Nature Conservancy Council not having the authority to override local interests. They have to consult all interested parties and this may be a very tedious and drawn out procedure. The NCC also have to find out what flora and fauna there is in the first place and to assess the ecology of the area. Local bye-laws have to be drawn up and old customs honoured. These are the criteria that the NCC have to abide by in order to designate a reserve. It is a pity that it has to work like that, since it wastes valuable time at the expense of the wildlife.

The NCC does not have the power, as do the authorities in New Zealand, to give blanket protection to an interesting area immediately, and then exclude everyone. By closing a likely area initially, the New Zealanders were able to watch and observe and build up a very detailed dossier of what wildlife gems were present. Surprises were at hand, some species built up to large populations. Fish grew to sizes never before seen. Fishermen were not antagonised since they were allowed to fish at the periphery. Their catches were good and they recognised that the protected area acted as a spawning ground for the replenishment of their fish. Furthermore, tourists came to look at the astonishing wildlife.

Local naturalists in England have long realised that many parts of our shores were rich and should be protected in a similar way to land-based sites. Public awareness of marine nature conservation was whipped up by the Marine Conservation Society, Greenpeace and Friends of the Earth. Voluntary nature conservation bodies and other interested parties set up their own marine reserves in the absence of any government support. Today twenty-seven county wildlife trusts have nature reserves with coastal frontage.

Some of these were voluntarily designated as marine nature reserves, but of course, without any state backing. Skomer Island off the Pembrokeshire coast was the first voluntary marine reserve, created in 1976 by the West Wales Trust. Purbeck in Dorset and Roseland on the south Cornwall coast followed. Others included Loch Sween (south-west Scotland), St Abbs (south-east Scotland), Flamborough Head (Yorkshire), Helford (south Cornwall), Bardsay Island (north Wales) and Strangford Lough (Northern Ireland).

With the Wildlife and Countryside Act of 1981 came powers to the NCC to recommend special marine areas worthy of conservation. Many such sites had been recognised in England, Scotland and Wales, but no MNR status was given to any, until 1986. The following are sites regarded as important by the NCC and may well be given special status in the future.

IMPORTANT MARINE ◆ NATURE RESERVE SITES ◆

Proposed site	Region	Proposed site	Region
The Monachs	Scotland, Outer Hebrides	Tidal rapids between Linne Mhuirich and Loch Sween	west Scotland
Lundy	Devon		
St Kilda Island	Outer Hebrides	Tidal rapids, Menai Strait	north Wales
Bardsey Island	Wales, Gwynedd		
Skomer Island	Wales, Dyfed	Marloes peninsula	Wales, Dyfed
Start Point	Devon	Lleyn peninsula	Wales, Gwynedd
Bembridge Ledges	Isle of Wight	Tresco sand-flats	Isles of Scilly
St Abb's Head	south-west Scotland	St Martins sand-flats	Isles of Scilly
Arisaig	west Scotland	Helford River	Cornwall
Sea-lochs	Scotland, Outer Hebrides	Percuil River	Cornwall

Lundy, an island in the Bristol Channel off the Devon coast was the first Marine Nature Reserve designated by the NCC. This famous milestone occurred in November 1986, when the Minister of the Environment, William Waldegrave officially visited the island. He had given an undertaking to create a MNR in 12–18 months, and did it in 13! Such is the British approach to nature conservation, that no less than 130 groups or individuals had to be consulted before the MNR could be given government backing, hence the delay.

Protected around Lundy are 1,650yd (1,500m) of shoreline. Overall Lundy has 10mi (16km) of shoreline and traditional potting for lobsters, crayfish and crabs can continue. An old right to fish off the shores given to local people under the Magna Carta of 1215 was upheld. This is the kind of administrative detail that New Zealand does not have to contend with. What makes Lundy so important are the warm-water-loving plants and animals like sunset star coral, jewel anemones, branching sponges and sea fans. There are rich communities of flora and fauna representative of warm waters, a nice mixture of Mediterranean and Atlantic type environments. Lying in the Bristol Channel, Lundy is warmed by the North Atlantic Drift.

All these other potential MNRs listed above have their own wildlife gems. We must seek to protect them before they disappear in the face of all the other activities which go on around our shores. After all, it is often the particular wildlife species which give the necessary criteria for a nature reserve to be formed in the first place. Not that it should be like this. Communities of common species are, arguably more important to keep going, than individual rare species, which may be on their way out anyway. So it is the suite of species found in particular ecological situations which is the key to nature conservation, whether it is on land or under the sea. The sea is the most unworked natural habitat left in Britain.

British territorial waters extend to 3mi (4.8km) from shore, so all MNRs have to be accommodated within this area. Threats to MNRs include harbour developments, marinas, activities such as water sports, mining and oil drilling. Pollution, whether from sewage effluent, oil or anti-fouling paints is obnoxious wherever it occurs. Fishermen using beam or otter trawls or scallop dredges disrupt and kill numerous other wildlife forms in their search for more food.

Finding out exactly what natural resources we have round our British shores is one of the major aims of the 2-year project called 'Coastwatch'. It was launched in March 1987 and at the time of writing is only half way through. It was funded with a donation of £48,000 from BP and backed by the Field Studies Council, the Conservation Society, the Royal Society for Nature Conservation and the WWF-UK. By the time this book appears the results may well be known. Both children and adults have been encouraged to walk their coast and find out what sorts of habitats are present, the diversity of wildlife (both plants and animals) and any problem to do with those habitats, e.g. bait-digging, sand extraction, waste disposal and recreation. The project has been a great success generating enormous voluntary participation. It has been excellent as a source of project work for GCSE exams work with special 'Coastwatch Days' and special Children's WATCH group outings.

Britain has 5,000mi (8,050km) of coastline and it has been divided into 9,672 coastal tetrads for recording purposes. By early 1988 the co-ordinators (the NCC) had over 1,513 volunteers. There will be many gaps to fill and no doubt the exercise will prove to be so popular it will provide teachers and children alike with other years of research on our coastal habitats.

At least Coastwatch will have whetted the appetite of youngsters to the wildlife and habitats on the coastline.

◆ AREAS OF OUTSTANDING NATURAL ◆ BEAUTY (AONBs)

These are much larger areas than SSSIs. In fact AONBs may contain numerous SSSIs within their limits. The reason for parcelling off larger areas of land is to conserve particular natural features. In fact the NCC, who have made the designations, state that the main purpose 'is to conserve and enhance "natural beauty", which includes protecting flora, fauna and geological as well as landscape features'. Flora and fauna does not always feature high in the policies for AONBs. Natural beauty, recreation, economic and social needs of local communities, agriculture and forestry are sometimes regarded as more important issues in AONBs.

AONBs go back to 1949 when thirty-five were designated under Section 87 of the National Parks and Access to the Countryside Act, 1949. The next AONB to be designated was the North Pennines AONB which was designated in 1979. The following year the Secretary of State named six other sites amongst which were the High Weald, the Camel estuary extension to Cornwall AONB and Cranborne Chase and West Wiltshire Downs. Priority is being given to proposed AONBs in the Clwydian Range and the Tamar and Tavy Valleys in Cornwall.

The largest AONB is the one on the North Wessex Downs at 668mi² (1,732km²), followed by the Cotswold AONB (582mi²/1,507km²) and the Dorset AONB (400mi²/1,036km²). Boundaries of AONBs may be adjusted in future years.

It is often curious the way in which conservation works. In March 1988 a farmer in Kent was awarded £38,851 in compensation so that he would not fell a 39a (15.6ha) wood. Trees in the wood had been previously given Tree Preservation Orders (TPOs) and it was incumbent upon the courts to uphold both the TPO regulations and the necessary requirement to conserve the 'natural beauty' of this part of an AONB (in this case the Kent Downs AONB).

Areas of Outstanding Natural Beauty, National Parks and The Broads (October 1988) – there are no AONBs in Scotland, just National Scenic Areas.

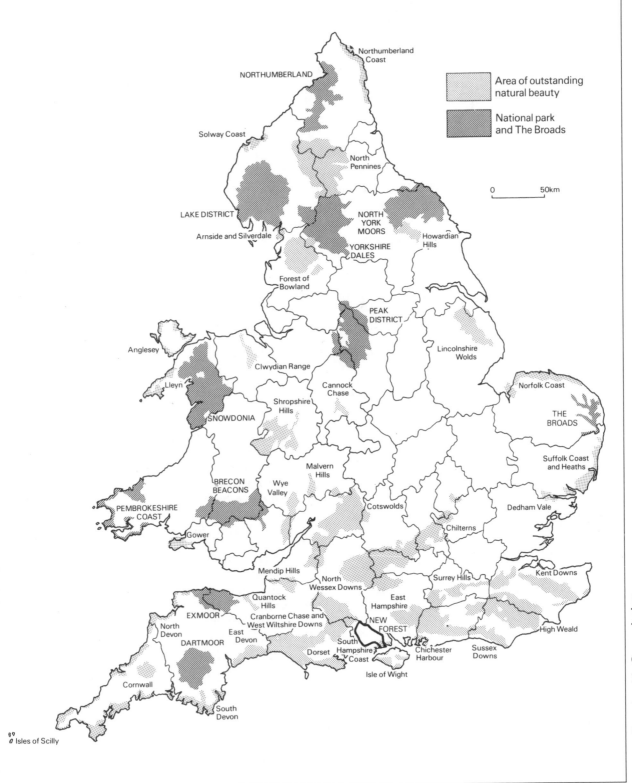

NORTHUMBERLAND

Northumberland
Coast

Solway Coast

North
Pennines

LAKE DISTRICT

Arnside and Silverdale

NORTH
YORK
MOORS

Howardian
Hills

YORKSHIRE
DALES

Forest of
Bowland

Anglesey

PEAK
DISTRICT

Lincolnshire
Wolds

Lleyn

Clwydian Range

Cannock
Chase

Norfolk Coast

SNOWDONIA

Shropshire
Hills

THE
BROADS

Suffolk Coast
and Heaths

BRECON
BEACONS

Malvern
Hills

Wye
Valley

Cotswolds

Dedham Vale

PEMBROKESHIRE
COAST

Chilterns

Gower

Kent Downs

Mendip Hills

North
Wessex Downs

Surrey Hills

Quantock
Hills

East
Hampshire

EXMOOR

Cranborne Chase and
West Wiltshire Downs

NEW
FOREST

High Weald

North
Devon

East
Devon

South
Hampshire
Coast

Chichester
Harbour

Sussex
Downs

DARTMOOR

Dorset

Cornwall

Isle of Wight

South
Devon

Isles of Scilly

Area of outstanding
natural beauty

National park
and The Broads

0   50km

Source: Countryside Commission

◆ ENVIRONMENTALLY SENSITIVE AREAS ◆
(ESAs)

These are large areas in which traditional agricultural methods are encouraged, so that 'scenic, historic and nature conservation interests' can be enjoyed. Like AONBs there may be several SSSIs within an ESA.

ESAs first gained popular interest when the Agriculture Bill went through committee stage in March 1986 and gave agriculture ministers the power to designate such areas. The advice of the NCC and Countryside Commissioners in both England and Wales and in Scotland was sought, and a list of fifty-six were proposed. In time it is hoped that all these will aspire to full ESA status, but eighteen were short-listed in Britain for further assessment. Then in February 1987 six were given status, followed by six more in May 1987.

◆ ESAs PROPOSED (1986) ◆
& DESIGNATED (1987)
(Those designated are underlined)

The numbers start with ESAs in Scotland, through to ESAs in the south of England.

1. Shetland
2. Orkney
3. Central Deeside
4. Caithness & NW Sutherland Coast
5. Uists & Benbecula
6. Inner Hebrides Coastal crofting & farming
7. Nithsdale
8. Breadalbane
9. Strathallan
10. Whitlaw/Eildon
11. Northumberland National Park Moorland
12. South Solway
13. North Pennines
14. Lake District
15. Arnside & Silverdale
16. Yorkshire Dales
17. North Yorks Moors
18. Lower Derwent Valley
19. Peak District
20. Shropshire Hills
21. Clun Valley
22. Wyre Forest
23. Nene Washes & Valley
24. Ouse Washes & Valley
25. Breckland
26. The Broads
27. Suffolk Coasts & Heaths
28. Dedham Vale
29. North Kent Marshes
30. North Downs
31. Ashdown Forest
32. Pevensey Levels
33. South Downs (east and west)
34. Surrey Heaths
35. Itchen Valley
36. Test Valley
37. New Forest grazings
38. North Wessex Downs
39. South Wiltshire Downs
40. Mendips
41. Somerset Levels & Moors
42. Exmoor
43. Dartmoor
44. Bodmin Moor
45. West Penwith Moors
46. Anglesey
47. Lleyn
48. Southern Snowdonia
49. East Montgomeryshire & East Radnorshire

The great appeal to farmers is that they do not have to pursue their high-tech methods of farming in such areas. There was some initial objection, especially in Yorkshire, but within a year many had signed up to take part. Eighty per cent of farmers in many areas are participating and receive grants varying from £12–160 an acre either to maintain existing grassland or to return arable land to grassland.

Farmers in ESAs have the greatest opportunities to diversify into all sorts of other areas. Tourism, amenity and visitor attractions, country crafts, farm products and shops, pony-trekking, livery and small scale sporting facilities. They will probably earn more money that way than from intensive arable farming.

The conservationists have argued for many things and won some concessions. We may well see some of the improved grassland areas reverting to a heathland type of scrub which has dramatically declined this century, and this will encourage wildlife. Not everything in nature conservation is taken up by the Ministry of Agriculture, Fisheries & Food. The Game Conservancy pushed for six-metre un-herbicided headlands to be part of the statute book on ESAs, but this was dropped at the last moment. Its inclusion would have been excellent for encouraging birds, butterflies, other insects and wild flowers at the edge of arable fields – the kind of work that the Game Conservancy is now engaged upon. The grey partridge has declined dramatically on the South Downs, where Dr Richard Potts now records 100 pairs instead of 850 pairs he saw 18 years ago.

◆ NATIONAL NATURE RESERVES (NNRs) ◆

There are 234 NNRs in England, Wales and Scotland. Their origins go back to 1915 when the Society for the Promotion of Nature Conservation (now the RSNC) recommended that they should be set up 'to preserve and maintain as part of the nation's heritage places which can be regarded as reservoirs for the main types of wild plants and animals represented in this country'.

NNRs tend to be some of the finest nature reserves in the land. They have always been designated by the NNC who act on behalf of the government. The NNC's aim has been to designate NNRs where the type of habitat is important, where there is an important range of flora and fauna and where there are rarities. The importance nationally and internationally is taken into consideration. In many cases the NNRs were chosen early on before the thousands of smaller nature reserves proliferated in Britain. Many NNRs today represent the cream of natural history sites in Britain.

NNRs are far more important than SSSIs, even Grade 1 SSSIs. Indeed, many NNRs may actually contain SSSIs of various descriptions. What makes a NNR different from a SSSI Grade I site is the fulfilment of various criteria. Conservationists like to discuss the merits of a certain site according to a basic set of ten criteria. There is much criticism, debate and argument over these criteria, but at least it serves as a basis for objective comparisons, sometimes subjective ones too. These are: (i) size, (ii) diversity, (iii) naturalness, (iv) rarity, (v) typicalness, (vi) fragility, (vii) recorded history, (viii) position in an ecological unit, (ix) potential value, and (x) intrinsic appeal.

The size of a nature reserve is a very critical issue, since you need at least a minimum of 10a (4ha) for the flora and fauna to breed successfully, rather than throwing up genetic imperfections through the necessity of in-breeding. Diversity of flora and fauna, whether there are lots of different species is an important issue on which a lot of weight is put. If the type of habitat represented by the NNR is rare nationally, or internationally, these would be good grounds for conservation. If there are rare species, such as natterjack toads or various butterflies these are good grounds too. It is interesting that our own criteria for nature conservation, i.e. that a site is stiff with orchids or full of a rare butterfly should influence our decision, but this is in fact the way in which we do formulate our conservation strategy. We are liable to forget that these criteria indicators may be present on a site which is man-managed and not on an original natural or semi-natural habitat. The desire to designate NNRs where the habitat shows a degree of 'naturalness' is not always satisfied since many NNRs are good examples of what man has done to a former, and often, completely different habitat on the same site.

To mention but a few NNRs in Britain, there are NNRs which protect rare habitats, such as the internationally important yew woods at Kingley Vale (West Sussex). Examples of wonderful chalk flora and fauna are to be found at Ashton Rowant NNR (Oxfordshire), Old Winchester Hill NNR (Hampshire) or the Wye and Crundale NNR (Kent), relic upland flora of the Upper Teasdale NNR (Durham), unique serpentine limestone ecology of the Lizard NNR (Cornwall) or wetland habitats for birds at Stodmarsh NNR (Kent).

At a more specific level, butterflies are offered sanctuary at Woodwalton Fen NNR and Monks Wood NNR both in Cambridgeshire and at Blean Woods NNR (Kent). Snake's head fritillaries are protected at north meadow, Cricklade NNR (Wiltshire) and gannets on the precipitous Noss NNR (Shetlands).

Man is the problem for NNRs. Fire is a major problem on heathland NNRs in the south and west. Hartland Moor NNR (Devon) lost 444a (180ha) of heather moor and the damage penetrated to 5ft (150cm) underground. Birds such as the Dartford warbler lost their territorial song posts on scrub bushes and Britain's rare reptiles such as the smooth snake and sand lizard have been lost from many sites through fire. Total habitat loss to farming, industry and urbanisation is another matter which hits hard on heathlands.

NNRs represent one of the richest collections of sites of British wildlife, our wildlife heritage. They represent about 395,200a (160,000ha). Half of the NNRs are in upland sites, and well over 44,460a (18,000ha) are salt marshes, mud-flats and sand-flats. The largest NNR in Britain is the Scottish Cairngorms (64,220a/26,000ha), the smallest is an archaeological site in north Kent, Swanscombe (5a/2ha).

The NNC only own about 25 per cent of the NNRs they have designated. The rest are part-owned, part-managed by the NCC or are leased or held under agreements with landowners. Sixteen NNRs are in the care of county wildlife trusts.

The threat of privatisation of NNRs is an insidious one. It reared its ugly head early in 1988 and is likely to affect all NNRs, not just the 25 per cent owned by the NCC. It has caused consternation within nature conservation circles. The thought of NNRs being sold off to private companies to exploit whatever they choose represents a direct threat to the cream of Britain's wildlife heritage. It is ironic that the government now wants to destroy the same NNRs which it asked the NCC to protect.

♦ SITES OF SPECIAL SCIENTIFIC INTEREST ♦
(SSSIs)

Almost 40 years after they were designated, SSSIs are still not clearly understood by the layman and people do not really know where their nearest SSSIs are. Despite this SSSIs continue to be mentioned almost daily in the newspapers. So what are they?

♦ What are SSSIs?

The acronym SSSI stands for Sites of Special Scientific Interest. They represent the gems of the countryside, the last stand for Britain's wildlife. They are graded into four groups from the prime sites (grade 1) of national or international importance, to grade 4 of lower regional importance. SSSIs were designated to pinpoint those highly sensitive areas that urban and industrial planners, farmers and foresters might avoid and leave us with some superb 'heritage' countryside. 'They are the special sites rich in flora, fauna or geological or physiographical features'. They often contain the last populations of rare native wild plants, rare invertebrates or have unique natural habitats. Above all they harbour a fantastic genetic pool of living material which has taken millions of years to evolve and which can become extinct overnight.

♦ How many SSSIs are there?

SSSIs were first designated in 1949. There were 4,085 of them in Great Britain (2,727 in England, 832 in Scotland and 528 in Wales) and in recent years each site has been reassessed for its importance by the Nature Conservancy Council (NCC), a task which is reaching 90 per cent coverage in some southern counties. With new SSSIs being designated and others being dropped the figure will soon be in the order of 6,000 SSSIs, representing about 8 per cent of the land surface of Great Britain.

♦ Where are SSSIs and can you visit them?

With so many SSSIs in Great Britain there must be some near you. How do you recognise them and find out where they are? Your regional NCC office carries a list but they are not always willing to supply you with one. They respect the private nature of many SSSIs. However, *bona fide* enquiries regarding specific SSSIs are often regarded sympathetically. Farmers are in a unique position of already owning or managing SSSI woods or meadows. Most know about the sensitivity of their sites but others will be told by the end of the new round of notification if they do not know already. The exhaustive job of the NCC has been to 'notify occupiers and owners of each SSSI about its precise whereabouts and draw attention to any potentially damaging operations which may affect the site'.

SSSIs can be ordinary looking woods, copses, meadows, heathlands or wetlands. Many are privately owned/managed by farmers, tenants of 'large' landowners, such as the Church or Crown Commissioners. More accessible ones are within national or country parks managed by the Countryside Commission or local councils. Others are exceedingly well protected and conserved on Ministry of Defence property – they take their conservation very seriously. Now that so many of us are members of the voluntary bodies such as the Royal Society for the Protection of Birds (RSPB), RSNC and the National Trust we all have an interest in and access to the numerous SSSIs which they own or manage. One third of all SSSIs belong to these bodies so in effect to us.

♦ How are SSSIs meant to be protected?

The NCC have a legal obligation to inform their councils where the SSSIs are and these are drawn on to their planning sheets. The planning office of the district council will also know where each SSSI is. If a new planning application falls within an SSSI the council then have a statutory obligation to inform the NCC who will advise them on their course of action. On the basis that the 6,000 or so SSSIs represent the bare minimum of habitats necessary to maintain the best examples of Britain's wildlife, the NCC always acts in the interests of conservation of wildlife and natural habitats. A submission to the council or to a public inquiry may be made by the NCC sometimes supported by voluntary conservation organisations like the RSPB or the RSNC.

♦ How fast are SSSIs disappearing?

SSSIs were disappearing at the alarming rate of 10–13 per cent per annum in 1981; 176 sites were damaged in 1983–4, 255 were damaged in 1984–5 and 174 in 1985–6. This is a deplorable loss for the extinction of genetic material tied up in the habitats lost and is of course unacceptable to lovers of the countryside. Approximately 7,500a (3,000ha) of the Broads wetlands rich in SSSIs have been ploughed up since the late 1960s. We all heard in the media of the herbiciding of West Mercia meadow (Essex) in 1985.

♦ Why are they disappearing?

The problem for wildlife is that it positively thrives on those rougher areas that farmers would like to bring into cultivation. The water meadows, wet woodlands and scrubby hillsides are the types of habitats that the government has offered financial incentives to drain in order to grow more food. There are also other important factors. Apart from agriculture, the NCC itemise forestry and 'other' activities which included skiiing (especially developments on the Cairngorms SSSI), motorcycle scrambling, fires and vandalism.

Draining land has always been good farming practice, but water authorities (up until privatisation) have always had a *carte blanche* to drain the land without asking the people. Our wetland wildlife on prime SSSIs such as Somerset Levels, North Kent Marshes, Nene washes (Cambridge) and the Derwent Ings (Ings are water meadows in Yorkshire), are under threat. Peat extraction in the Moss of Rora damaged two SSSIs. Rougher pastures have attracted grants to improve them (not for wildlife but for agriculture!). Grants were given to farmers for ploughing and grubbing sites into production. The tragedy has been the loss of 1,000-year-old SSSI meadows with the passage of a single plough, let alone herbicide.

Forestry has eliminated many SSSIs and is even more undesirable if it is done with tax advantages. The government can overrule protection afforded to SSSIs. For instance, the Forestry Commission and Secretary of State for Scotland can approve a forestry planting scheme even on the prime Flow Country of Sutherland and Caithness. About one seventh of the world's blanket bog is in Britain.

A sort of rationing system of ecologically-interesting sites nationwide has been discussed, but not adopted. If one region has too much of one particular habitat it may be encouraged to short-list the best parts for protection, whilst others may be expendable. For instance, a Scottish county may have a surfeit of bogs compared to Kent and could easily 'afford' to lose several of its bogs. In reverse, Kent is very short of bogs and could not afford to lose any. However, it does have lots of chalk grassland habitats. How many of these could be expendable?

◆ Farmers and conservation

All is not gloom, doom, death and destruction in the countryside. Farmers are not all bad. How can we continue with intensive agriculture and protect wildlife? The answer is in an integrated approach – assistance is available. There is of course, the other side of the argument, the farmers' point of view. There are 55 million mouths to be fed in Britain and agriculture must continue, whatever EEC constraints are forced upon it.

Most farmers will do their best to promote wildlife and habitats without putting themselves out of business. Farmers cannot survive on birds and bees. It is only a minority of farmers who directly disregard the law. Everyone is then obliged to look at the havoc they have inflicted. Of course, friction is generated between conservationists and farmers but a wonderful liaison group called FWAG, the Farming & Wildlife Advisory Group bridges the gap and advises farmers of the best things to do to encourage wildlife. There is a FWAG-person near every farmer now. Farmers have been busy in recent years planting spinneys, hedges and restoring ponds and getting in the news for winning awards for promoting wildlife on farms.

◆ What is being done to stop SSSI destruction?

The Ministry of Agriculture, Fisheries and Food and the Countryside Commission embarked on a 3-year trial period from 1985 of paying farmers not to farm on prime ecological sites. In their first year they paid out a subsidy of £50 an acre on 8,403a (3,402ha). Survey work by the NCC is continuing. In 1987 we will see the completion of their nationwide ancient woodland SSSI survey.

We may not be able to move food mountains, but we can certainly move SSSI meadows. Both the Sainsbury's and Tesco supermarket chains have enjoyed the publicity of funding the turf by turf movement of SSSI meadows in Suffolk and Warwickshire to make way for their food halls. Are our priorities right? Will we keep our wildlife while we keep shoving it around?

◆ What can you do?

It is really incumbent upon everyone who loves the country to find out where their nearest SSSIs are. Once you know their whereabouts, be alert to local applications that may affect those sites (which are considered at parish council meetings). Lodge objections against such proposals and telephone your local regional NCC office for more information. 'People power' really works, Amberley Wildbrooks SSSI was won for the villagers of Amberley in West Sussex.

SSSIs continue to make daily headlines. Every day we learn more about threats to our SSSIs and we wonder whether we have a say in how our countryside will fare or if our opinions are headed, whether it is the Shakespeare Cliffs SSSI or the Holywell Coombe SSSI threatened by the channel tunnel development, the Wych Farm oilfield at Poole Harbour (Dorset) whose Fawley pipeline will cross seven SSSIs and two NNRs, the Morrich More SSSI, the Okehampton bypass (Devon) or the Dersingham bypass (Norfolk). How much effort can you give to the protection of the rural countryside? Can you encourage the government to give more money to the NCC to protect our rich heritage? The more people who support voluntary conservation bodies, the better our chances to keep green England's pleasant land.

Youth organisations are actively employed nationwide in the control of invasive scrub.

FURTHER
READING

• MEADOWS •

Brown V. K. (1983) *Grasshoppers* Naturalist's Handbook No. 2, Cambridge University Press

Greenoak F. (1985) *God's Acre*, Orbis/WI

Hare T. (1988) *London's Meadows and Pastures (Neutral Grassland)* Ecology Handbook 8, London Ecology Unit

Hepper F. N. (1987) *Planting a Bible Garden*, Her Majesty's Stationery Office

Lousley J. E. (1969) *Wild Flowers of Chalk & Limestone* Collins, New Naturalist

Mabey R. & Evans T. (1980) *The Flowering of Britain*, Hutchinson

Measures D. G. (1976) *Bright Wings of Summer*, Cassell

Johnson A. T. & Smith H. A. (1979) *Plant Names Simplified*, Landsmans Bookshop Ltd, Herefordshire

Perring F. H. & Farrell L. (1983) *Vascular Plants* 2nd Edition, British Red Data Books: 1

Robinson W. (1880) *God's Acre Beautiful: or the Cemeteries of the Future*, The Garden Office, Scriber & Welford

Robinson W. (1977) *The Wild Garden*, The Scolar Press

Royal Society for Nature Conservation (1983) *Disappearing Wildflowers*

Wells D. A. & Oswald P. H. (1988) *The Conservation of Meadows and Pastures*, Nature Conservancy Council

◆ WOODLANDS, TREES AND BOGS ◆

ADAS (1984) *Farm Woodland*, Ministry of Agriculture, Fisheries & Food

Brooks A. (1980) *Woodland*, British Trust for Conservation Volunteers

Dalton S. (1986) *The Secret Life of an Oakwood – A Photographic Essay*, Century

Edlin H. L. (1978) *Trees, Woods and Man*, Collins

Elton J. (1966) *The Patterns of Animal Communities*, Methuen

Forestry Commission (1985) *Guidelines for the Management of Broad-leaved Woodland*, Forestry Commission

FWAG (1986) *Trees on Farms in the Lowlands*, Farming & Wildlife Advisory Group, Leaflet No. 21.

Mabey R. (1983) *Oak & Company*, Kestrel

Mitchell A. (1984) *A Field Guide to the Trees of Britain and Europe*, Collins

Rackham O. (1980) *Ancient Woodland*, Arnold, London

Rackham O. (1986a) *Trees and Woodland in the British Landscape*, Dent

Rackham O. (1986b) *The Ancient Woodland of England: the Woods of South-East Essex*, Rochford District Council, Rochford, Essex

Ratcliffe D. A. & Oswald P. H. (1987) *Birds, Bogs & Forestry*, Nature Conservancy Council

Wilkinson G. (1981) *A History of British Trees*, Hutchinson

◆ HEDGEROWS ◆

Angus A. (1987) *Hedgerow*, Partridge Press

Brandon P. (1974) *The Sussex Landscape*, Hodder & Stoughton

Brooks A. (1984) *Hedging*, British Trust for Conservation Volunteers

Dowdeswell W. H. (1987) *Hedgerows and Verges*, Allen & Unwin

Feltwell J. (1986) *The Natural History of Butterflies*, Croom Helm

Hooper M. D. (1970) 'The Botanical Importance of Hedgerows' In *The Flora of a Changing Britain* (ed. by Perring F. H.), Botanical Society of the British Isles

Mabey R. (1974) *The Roadside Wildlife Book*, David & Charles

Ministry of Agriculture, Fisheries and Food (1980) *Managing Farm Hedges*, Leaflet 762

Muir R. & N. (1987) *Hedgerows*, Michael Joseph

Nature Conservancy Council (1976) *Hedges and Shelterbelts*, Nature Conservation Guides

Pollard E., Hooper M. D. & Moore N. W. (1974) *Hedges*, Collins

Rackham O. (1976) *Trees and Woodland in the British Landscape*, Dent & Sons Ltd. (*see* chapter 10, 'Trees on the Farm: Hedges and Elsewhere').

Shoard M. (1980) *The Theft of the Countryside*, Temple Smith (*see* chapter 3, 'Hedgerows in Part Two').

Thomas E. & White J. T. (1980) *Hedgerow*, Ash & Grant

Wilson R. (1979) *The Hedgerow Book*, David & Charles

◆ THE ORGANIC GARDEN AND FARM ◆

Buczacki S. (1987) *Ground Rules for Gardeners, a Practical Guide to Garden Ecology*, Collins

Carson R. (1962) *Silent Spring*, Penguin

Gear A. (1987) *The New Organic Food Guide*, Dent

Graham F. (1970) *Since Silent Spring*, Pan

Hamilton G. (1988) *Successful Organic Gardening*, Dorling Kindersley

Hay J. (1987) *Natural Pest and Diseases Control*, Century

Hay J. (1987) *Vegetables Naturally – Organic Growing for Small Gardens*, Century

Henry Doubleday Research Association (1988) *The Complete Organic Gardening Catalogue, 1988*, HDRA

Kitto D. (1986) *Planning the Organic Vegetable Garden*, Thorsons

Nelson S. (1988) *Organic Gardening Country Calendar and Planning Guide*, Thorsons

Philbrick H. & Gregg R. (1974) *Companion Plants*, Watkins

Stickland S. (1986) *Planning the Organic Flower Garden*, Thorsons

Wookey B. (1987) *Rusthall, The Story of an Organic Farm*, Blackwell

◆ FARMING ARABLE AND FRUIT ◆

Countdown on Nitrates (1987) Proceedings of the conference on 20 November, 1986, organised by the Council for Environmental Conservation

Tittensor R. & A. (1986) *Nature Conservation for Busy Farmers*, Walberton Green House, Arundel, E. Sussex BN18 0QB

◆ LINEAR RESERVES ◆

Mabey R. (1974) *The Roadside Wildlife Book*, David & Charles

Morris P. (1983) *Hedgehogs*, Whittet Books

Pick C. (1984) *Off The Motorway*, Cadogan & Century Books

Sargent C. (1984) *Britain's Railway Vegetation*, Institute of Terrestrial Ecology

◆ WILDLIFE SANCTUARIES ◆

Baines C. (1984) *A Guide to Habitat Creation*, GLC Ecology Handbook No. 2

Baines C. (1987) *How to Make a Wildlife Garden*, Hamish Hamilton

Berry R. (1981) 'Town Mouse, Country Mouse: adaptation and adaptability', *Mammal Review* 11 (3) 91–136

Burton J. (1983) *Flora of the London Area*, London Natural History Society

Camazine S. (1987) *The Naturalist's Year*, John Wiley, Chichester (25 outdoor explorations)

Chambers J. (1989) *Wild Flower Gardening* WI/Ward Lock

Dartington A. (1969) *The Ecology of Rubbish Tips*, Heinemann

Davies B. N. K. (1982) *Ecology of Quarries*, Institute of Terrestrial Ecology

Feltwell, J. (1987) *The Naturalist's Garden*, Ebury

Forster N. (1987) *Conservation in School Grounds*, British Trust for Conservation Volunteers

Hansen G. (1979) *Life Among The Nettles*, Wayland

Mabey R. (1976) *Street Flowers*, Kestrel

Marren P. (1982) *A Natural History of Aberdeen*, Callander, Haughend, Finzean

Norfolk Naturalists' Trust (1988) *Wildlife Conservation in Churchyards* (from 72 Cathedral Close, Norwich, Norfolk NR1 4DF)

Nicholson-Lord D (1988) *The Greening of the Cities*, Routledge & Kegan

Read M. (1988) *The English Vicarage Garden*, Michael Joseph

Smith D. (1984) *Urban Ecology*, Practical Ecology Series, Allen & Unwin

Stevens J. (1987) *The National Trust Book of Wildflower Gardening*, Dorling Kindersley

◆ INTERPRETATION ◆

Green B. (1981) *Countryside Conservation*, The Resource Management Series, 3, Allen & Unwin

Her Majesty's Stationery Office (1981) *Wildlife and Countryside Act 1981*, HMSO

Mabey R. (1980) *The Common Ground. A Place for Nature in Britain's Future*, Hutchinson in association with the Nature Conservancy Council

Moore N. W. (1987) *The Bird of Time. The Science and Politics of Nature Conservation*, Cambridge

Porritt J. (1984) *Seeing Green*, Basil Blackwell.

Pye-Smith C. & Rose C. (1984) *Crisis and Conservation, Conflict in the British Countryside*, Pelican

Shoard M. (1980) *The Theft of the Countryside*, Temple Smith

Shoard M. (1987) *This Land is Our Land*, Paladin

Warren A. & Goldsmith F. B. (1983) *Conservation in Perspective*, John Wiley

FURTHER INFORMATION

• MEADOWS •

Botanical Society of the British Isles (BSBI), The Hon. General Secretary, Dep't of Botany, British Museum (Natural History), Cromwell Road, London SW7 5BD. The principal botanical society in the country representing amateurs and professionals.

Emorsgate Seeds, Terrington St Clement, Nr Kings Lynn, Norfolk PE34 4NY. Tel. 0553-829028. Catalogue available.

John Chambers Seeds, 15 Westleigh Road, Barton Seagrave, Kettering, Northamptonshire NN15 5AJ. Tel. 0933-681632. Catalogue available.

London Ecology Unit, Berkshire House, 168–173 High Holborn, London WC1V 7AG. Tel. 01-379-4352, 01-379-0608

Nature Conservancy Council (NCC), Interpretive Services Branch, Peterborough PE1 1UA. Tel. 0733-40345. Numerous publications listed in catalogue.

The Royal Society for Nature Conservation, The Green, Nettleham, Lincoln LN2 2NR. Tel. 0522-752326. (48 trusts, 180,000 members, 1,680 reserves in England, Wales, Scotland, Northern Ireland, Isle of Man and Guernsey.) You automatically become a member of this if you become a member of the local wildlife trust.

Wild Flower Society, 68 Outwoods Road, Loughborough LE11 3LY

Primrose

• WOODLANDS, TREES AND BOGS •

British Trust for Conservation Volunteers (BTCV), Publications, Jim Chanter, 12 Winchester Gardens, Andover, Hampshire. Tel. 0264-53252

Council for the Protection of Rural England (CPRE), 4 Hobart Place, London SW1W 0HY. Tel. 01-235-9481

Farming & Wildlife Advisory Service (FWAG) (*see* page 00)

National Trust (NT), 36 Queen's Gate, London, SW1H 9AS. Tel. 01-222-9251.

Men of the Trees, Freepost, Crawley Down, Crawley, W. Sussex RH10 4HL. Tel. 0342-712536. Dedicated to planting trees in the United Kingdom and throughout the world.

The Tree Council, 35 Belgrave Square, London SW1X 8QN. Tel. 01-235-8854. Keep Britain a green and pleasant land by becoming a friend of the council and receive the tri-annual *Tree News*. The council has a number of useful publications and is supported by many professional conservation bodies.

Woodland Trust, Westgate, Grantham, Lincolnshire NG31 6LL. Tel. 0476-74297

• HEDGEROWS •

British Trust for Conservation Volunteers (see above)

• THE ORGANIC GARDEN AND FARM •

Chase Organics, Addlestone Way, Weybridge, Surrey KT15 1HY. Tel. 0932-858511. Market seeds and organic materials for the garden.

Earthworms (i) Wonderworms, Pine Trees Farm, Hubberton, Sowerby Bridge, West Yorks HX6 1NT. Tel. 0422-831112. Make kits for

Pansy

making compost out of paper, cardboard, waste vegetables and spoiled straw, 19 years experience mainly for farmers. (ii) British Ground Baits, 4 Elm Mill, Bardsield Saling, Nr. Braintree, Essex CM7 2EJ. Tel. 0371-850247

Farm Verified Organic, 86 Easton Street, High Wycombe, Bucks HP11 1LJ. Tel. 0494-4599922. A group which seeks to maintain high standards of organic produce; works in close association with the Soil Association and the Organic Farmers and Growers.

National Centre for Organic Gardening, Ryton-on-Dunsmore, Coventry CV8 3LG. Tel. 0203-303517. A research institution and charity (11,000 members) where organic procedures are put to practice; everything from kitchen gardens, herbaceous beds, rose gardens, compost making and mulching. Open every day except Christmas Day and Boxing Day. Five-star, highly recommended.

Nature et Progrès, 14 rue de la Goncourt, Paris 75115. A strong association of regional groups dedicated to organic farming and healthy environment; impressive book and leaflet list of over 200 titles.

Organic Farmers and Growers Ltd (OF & G), Abacus House, Station Road, Needham Market, Ipswich, Suffolk IP6 8AT. Tel. 0449-720838. Sets standards and monitors procedures now in conjunction with the Soil Association. With more than 200 members (mid-1988) they represent the largest producers of organic produce in the United Kingdom. They publish *The Organic Handbook* (£5).

The Soil Association, 86–88 Colston Street, Bristol BS1 5BB. Tel. 0272-290661. A charity (4,000 members) which seeks to protect the environment and grow healthy food. After becoming a member you can display the Soil Association symbol after your farm or small-holding has been inspected and certified to certain minimum standards.

Women's Farming Union, Joan Cremer, WFU Central Office, Crundalls, Matfield, Kent TN12 7EA. Tel. 089272-2803. There are 21 regional groups (from Scotland to Cornwall) who run a weekly retail surveillance scheme to monitor top fruit, potatoes and dairy products in British supermarkets, and are pressing for government definitions of 'natural', 'real' and 'organic' foods. They make the link between producer and consumer.

Organic food: Oliver's Wholefood Store, 243 Munster Road, London SW6. Tel. 01-381-5477. Organic wine from France, Germany, Italy as well as other organic foods.

◆ FARMING ARABLE AND FRUIT ◆

Committee for Environmental Conservation (CoEnCo), 80 York Way, London N1 9AG. Tel. 01-278-4736/7. Publish *Habitat*, a worthwhile digest of conservation and ecological facts and reviews.

Farming & Wildlife Advisory Groups (FWAG), c/o RSPB, The Lodge, Sandy, Beds SG19 2DL. Tel. 0767-80551. Publishes 24 free leaflets on many diverse subjects from roadside verge management, general countryside conservation and landscape to conservation of butterflies, otters and owls.

Ministry of Agriculture, Fisheries & Food, Head Office, Great Westminster House, Horseferry Road, London SW1. Tel. 01-216-6135

National Farmers' Union, Agriculture House, Knightsbridge, London SW1X 7NJ. Tel. 01-235-5077

Royal Society for the Protection of Birds (RSPB), The Lodge, Sandy, Beds SG19 2DL. Tel. 0767-80551. Encourage the conservation of wild birds with half a million members, manage 125 nature reserves, run Young Ornithologists' Club (YOC) (see page 155).

Game Conservancy, Fordingbridge, Hampshire SP6 1EF. Tel. 0425-52381. A research and advisory group which has produced 20 useful books, leaflets and guides to habitat management, ecology and conservation on birds, goose, partridge, pheasant and woodcock management, game pests and mammals, deer, rabbits, squirrels and fish. Major involvement in new forms of land use, set-aside, extensification and field margin management.

The Otter Trust, Earsham, Bungay, Suffolk NR35 2AF. Tel. 0986-3470. Also a branch of the trust in Cornwall at North Petherwin (Navarino) near Launceston (north Cornwall). The conservation of otters is one of the major aims of the Otter Trust. Breeding and release to the wild has been one of the successes of the trust. Interpretive Centre at Bungay set around the River Waveney and three lakes.

◆ LINEAR RESERVES ◆

British Hedgehog Preservation Society, Knowbury House, Knowbury, Shropshire. Publishes a newsletter for friends of the society, and raises money for construction of hedgehog ramps.

Flora and Fauna Preservation Society, c/o Zoological Society of London, Regents Park, London NW1 4RY. Tel. 01-586-0872. Publishes *Oryx* and *Bat News* a quarterly newsletter. There are over 70 local bat groups.

The London Wildlife Trust, 80 York Way, London N1 9AG. Tel. 01-278-6612. The most thriving of all urban conservation groups with 30 wildlife sites in the Greater London area. It has local groups in all the London boroughs.

◆ WILDLIFE SANCTUARIES ◆

Flora & Fauna Preservation Society (see above).

Golf Course Wildlife Trust, 17–19 Stratford Place, London W1N 9AF. Tel. 01-409-8099

London Wildlife Trust (see above)

Sanctuary, Conservation Bulletin of the MOD. Send for details to MOD Conservation Officer, PL (Lands) 3, Room B3/21, Government Buildings, Leatherhead Road, Chessington, Surrey KT9 2LU

Young Ornithologist's Club (YOC), The Lodge, Sandy, Beds SG19 2DL. Tel. 0767-80551. Over 102,000 members, 700 local groups and leaders, holiday camps, members' days, membership £4 p.a. (1988), age group from 9–14, though up to 18 taken. Free arm-band and bi-monthly *Bird Life* on membership.

Wild daffodil

◆ INTERPRETATION ◆

Cetacean Group of the UK Mammal Society, c/o The Linnean Society, Burlington House, Piccadilly, London W1V 0LQ

Coastwatch, co-ordinated by the Nature Conservancy Council, Northminster House, Peterborough PE1 1UA

Conservation Society, 12a Guildford Street, Chertsey, Surrey KT16 9BQ. Tel. 09328-60975.

Countryside Commission, John Dower House, Crescent Place, Cheltenham, Gloucestershire GL50 3RA. Tel. 0242-21381. An independent body funded by the Department of the Environment. Publications (catalogue on request) from Publications Despatch Dep't, 19/23, Albert Road, Manchester MI9 2EQ

Department of the Environment, Room B3, Publications Unit, Dep'ts of Environment and Transport, Victoria Road, Ruislip, Middlesex HA4 0NZ. Tel. 01-845-1200

Field Studies Council, Preston Montford, Montford Bridge, Shrewsbury, Salop SY4 1HW. Tel. 0743-85064. Organise excellent (residential) courses on a wide variety of ecological subjects at their regional field study centres.

Friends of the Earth (FOE), 377 City Road, London EC1V 1NA. Tel. 01-837-0731

Greenpeace, 30-31 Islington Green, London N1 8XE. Tel. 01-354-5100

Marine Conservation Society, 4 Gloucester Road, Ross-on-Wye HR9 5BU. Tel. 0989-66017. A registered charity. Publishes *The Good Beach Guide*.

INDEX

Figures in *italics* refer to illustrations

⋅ WHAT IS THE WI? ⋅

If you have enjoyed this book, the chances are that you would enjoy belonging to the largest women's organisation in the country – the Women's Institutes.

We are friendly, go-ahead, like-minded women, who derive enormous satisfaction from all the movement has to offer. This list is long – you can make new friends, have fun and companionship, visit new places, develop new skills, take part in community services, fight local campaigns, become a WI market producer, and play an active role in an organisation which has a national voice.

The WI is the only women's organisation in the country which owns an adult education establishment. At Denman College, you can take a course in anything from car maintenance to paper sculpture, from book-binding to yoga, or word processing to the martial arts.

All you need to do to join is write to us here at the **National Federation of Women's Institutes, 39 Eccleston Street, London SW1W 9NT**, or telephone 01-730 7212, and we will put you in touch with WIs in your immediate locality.

About the author

Dr John Feltwell is a naturalist whose prolific output includes six books published over the last three years (he also has 70 scientific papers and an academic textbook in print), reviewing, broadcasting and research work for the BBC (he worked on Attenborough's *First Eden*) and lecturing on all aspects of the living world. In 1978, he set up *Wildlife Matters* to promote conservation and education and he also runs the *Wildlife Matters Photographic Library*. John Feltwell is a fellow of the Royal Entomological Society of London, Member of the Royal Horticultural Society, Chartered Member of the Institute of Biology and he also belongs to numerous conservation organisations.